Keys to Reading

Air Pudding and Wind Sauce

Theodore L. Harris
Mildred Creekmore
Louise Matteoni

Harold B. Allen
Linguistic Consultant

THE ECONOMY COMPANY
Oklahoma City   Atlanta   Indianapolis

Cover design by McRay Magleby
Cover illustration by Ron Eddington
Graphic Communications, Brigham Young University Press

ISBN 0–87892–438–8

Contents

Tricks, Traps, and Deals

Footprints

The Wonder of It

Mountain Echoes

City High, City Low

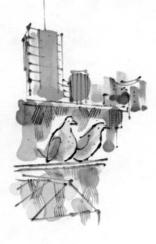

The Wise and the Foolish

tricks, traps, and deals

heels   leaped   sheet   lain
cone   chose   state   prize

treat
Kate
replied
crept
circus
dial

Kate and the Big Cat

7

On the Loose

Kate set a large sack on the table. "Mom, can't I please stay here while you and Dad go back to get the new kitchen curtain?" she asked.

"Stay here alone? In this apartment?" her mother replied. "Why, Kate, there's no one else around, and we have no phone."

"Oh, Mom, I'm not a baby," Kate said. "Besides, if I stay here, I can get started unpacking. Oh, please, can't I stay?" Kate added, turning to her dad.

"Well, if you could start unpacking, it would be a big help, Kate," said Dad. "But besides getting a new kitchen curtain, we need to get someone to put in our phone. So we may be gone for some time."

"I'll be okay, Dad. I'm sure I will," replied Kate. "I've started unpacking some of these boxes already. And I can put away the fresh meat, too."

"Well, I guess you may stay," replied her mother. "But don't leave the building."

Kate went with Mother and Dad to the car. "Remember. Don't leave until we get back," Dad said as they drove away.

"Okay," said Kate. But she did wish her mother and dad wouldn't treat her so much like a baby. "They're the same as always," she thought.

Kate sighed softly as she watched the car pull onto the highway. She had thought that things would really be different when she moved to this new place. "But if they're going to treat me like a baby, everyone else will, too," Kate thought. "It'll be just like it was at the old apartment." And she sighed once more.

As Kate walked along the hall of the new building, she opened a door here and there to see what the rest of the new building was like. She opened one door, and there on the floor in the empty room was a phone. "Hmm, Mom and Dad didn't know there was already a phone here," she said to herself. "The men must have used it when they were working on the building."

Kate went back to the apartment and began unpacking the boxes in the kitchen. As she climbed up and down putting things away, she got hot and tired. So she went outside to get some fresh air.

Kate sat on the front steps and watched the cars going by on the highway. Suddenly her attention was caught by a long line of trucks headed toward the city. The trucks were bright red, white, and blue.

"Those are circus trucks!" Kate cried.

Kate stared as the trucks moved along. She knew each truck carried cages of circus animals. If she stared hard enough as they passed by, she might be able to see the animals inside the cages.

Suddenly Kate stared at only one truck. The door on its cage kept sliding open and shut! Then the door stayed wide open. A large animal poked its head out the door, and Kate saw its yellow and black stripes. "A tiger!" she whispered softly.

The big animal looked all around. Then it jumped from the truck and headed into the tall grass along the highway.

The circus trucks kept moving slowly on. "Oh, my! No one else saw what happened!" cried Kate. "What can I do?"

11

The tiger crept out of the tall grass and headed toward the apartment buildings. Then it crept into a large clump of bushes near the apartments. "What can I do?" Kate kept saying over and over.

Then Kate thought of the phone in the empty room. Quickly she ran down the hall and picked up the phone. She heard a dial tone hum in her ear, and she quickly began spinning the dial.

"Give me the police, please!" Kate almost shouted.

A second later a steady voice said, "This is Officer Brown."

"Tiger! There's a tiger in some bushes in front of our apartment," cried Kate.

"Did you say 'tiger'?" the policeman asked. Then he said, "Look, little girl, I don't have time for games. Why don't you just go outside and play? You know better than to play with the phone."

Then Kate heard the dial tone again. The policeman did not believe her! Kate was all alone with a real tiger walking around just outside her apartment building.

Trapped!

Kate was frightened as she put the phone back on its hook. The tiger was outside, and the police thought she was playing a game! What could she do?

Kate looked to see if the tiger was still there. Yes, it was—she saw it crouched in the bushes, looking fierce.

What if a small child came along? And how were Mother and Dad going to get inside when they came home?

Then Kate saw the line of garage doors that lay between her and the tiger. Mother and Dad had left their garage door open. Since that garage door could be locked from the outside, Kate decided she might be able to capture the fierce tiger.

She went rushing to the kitchen and chose a ham from one of the boxes. Then she ran to the garage. She threw the ham inside and then hurried back to the apartment. Quickly she opened some fresh meat. She cut one pound into chunks, then another. Then, one by one, she threw the chunks of meat onto the driveway.

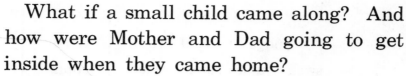

Soon the meat made a trail between the tiger and the garage door. Then as hard as she could, Kate threw a chunk of meat out toward the tiger. The meat plopped near the driveway, right in front of the bushes.

Everything was still. Then the fierce tiger leaped out of the bushes. And in one bite the hungry animal ate the chunk of meat. Then it sniffed from side to side for more. Kate threw another chunk near the open garage door. The tiger leaped again. Now it was on the driveway.

Little by little the hungry animal came across the driveway, eating each chunk of meat. Soon it had eaten its way to the garage door. Would it smell the ham inside?

15

"Oh, no!" Kate moaned as the tiger stopped just outside the garage. Like a big cat, it curled up and began to clean its paws.

"Tiger! Tiger! Don't go to sleep!" Kate begged softly. "Go on inside!"

But the tiger seemed to have eaten enough already. It stretched and looked sleepy. What could Kate do now? She had to get the tiger into the garage.

Then Kate's thoughts went back to the pots and pans she had put away. But if she stood in the door making noise with those pots and pans, the tiger was sure to see her. "You said you were not a baby. Now prove it," she told herself.

So she ran to the kitchen and chose two large pans.

Kate threw one pan out onto the driveway and beat the other with her hand. At the loud clang, the tiger leaped to its feet. Then it ran inside the garage.

In a second Kate was outside. She yanked on the rope of the garage door, and the door came down with a bang. She quickly turned the handle to lock it. At last she had the tiger in her trap!

Before long, Kate's mother and dad came home. Kate was watching for them.

"Oh, Kate! You're safe!" her dad called as he drove into the driveway. "We just now heard that a circus tiger got away near these new apartment buildings."

"I know all about the tiger," Kate said, still a little frightened, "since I have him caught there in the garage."

17

"There? In the garage?" her mother and dad said at the same time. Then, from inside the garage, they heard the soft footsteps of the tiger, then an angry roar.

"Yes, there in the garage," Kate replied, trying to sound as if she had not done a thing important. "I decided to capture him myself."

Kate told her dad about the phone that had been left in the apartment building. And Dad went rushing inside to call the police. Soon a circus truck came and took the tiger away.

When all was quiet again, Kate's mother had a new, proud look in her eyes. "I can't get over that child," she kept saying to Dad. "What was she trying to prove when she decided to capture that tiger alone?"

"Child, nothing!" Kate's dad answered. "Anyone who can trap a tiger by herself is not a child. We'll have to treat Kate like a lady from now on."

Kate felt warm inside when she saw that proud look in her dad's eyes, too. This was going to be a great place to live!

Phillips   Murphy   phonograph
workable   usable   movable
cell   bicycle   decide

carriage   antique

telephone
valuable
certainly
Eddie
enjoyable
quarter
property
piece
rubbish

Any Old Junk Today?

19

Never a week went by that Eddie Wilson didn't bring home a piece of something he called "valuable property." But his father called it junk.

All the family knew when Eddie brought home some of this valuable property. At dinner he would always say, "I had a very enjoyable day today."

"Now, see here, Eddie!" said his father one day. "This junk collecting has to stop! Every week the neighbors put out all their rubbish, and every Saturday you bring most of that rubbish to our house. Now I'm tired of it."

"You were glad when I brought home the telephone pole," Eddie said.

"Well, that was different," Mr. Wilson said. "I could use that pole. But this junk collecting has got to stop. We'll never get all that junk out of your room."

"But, Dad!" said Eddie. "It's my valuable property."

"Valuable property!" said Eddie's father. "Junk! All you bring home is junk!"

"Even the telephone pole?" said Eddie.

"Well," his father said, "that's the only thing we were ever able to use."

The next Saturday Mr. Wilson took Mrs. Wilson and Eddie shopping. They drove for a while before Mr. Wilson stopped in front of a shop. Over the door of the shop was a sign that said ANTIQUES. Eddie was able to read most signs. But he couldn't read that one.

"What does that sign say?" he asked.

"Antiques," answered his father.

"Are we going to see Aunt Teek?" Eddie asked. "Does she own this shop?"

"Not Aunt Teek," laughed Mr. Wilson. "But antiques. Antiques are old things. The sign means that this shop has all kinds of old things to sell."

"You mean junk?" asked Eddie.

"Certainly not!" said Mr. Wilson. "Eddie, antique things are very valuable. They sell for a lot of money."

Eddie and his father and mother walked up to the shop. Boxes on the front steps were full of all kinds of old things.

"It looks like junk to me!" said Eddie.

The inside of the shop was full of more old things. "I can find a piece of very valuable property here!" Eddie thought.

Eddie's father and mother talked to the shopkeeper while Eddie wandered around. He looked at shelf after shelf of old things. Then he wandered through a door into the back of the shop.

"Hello, son!" said a man stacking boxes. "Can I help you?"

"I'm just looking around," said Eddie.

Then all at once Eddie saw something that looked like valuable property. High on a shelf stood an old carriage lamp. It was rusty and covered with dust.

"Do you want to sell that lamp?" Eddie asked the man.

"Oh, I guess we could," he answered.

"How much is it?" asked Eddie.

"Oh, twenty-five cents would be enough," said the man.

Eddie took his money from his pocket. He had seventy-five cents. "Okay," he said. "I'll take it!"

The man took the lamp from the shelf.

Just then Eddie saw something with wheels. "What is that?" he asked.

"That's an old coffee grinder," the man answered.

"Those are swell wheels on it!" Eddie said. "What's the price?"

"Oh, I guess you can have it for about two quarters," the man replied.

"Then I'll take it, too," said Eddie.

The man blew the dust off the carriage lamp and put it into a box with the coffee grinder. The end of the lamp wouldn't go in, but he covered the box with a lid and tied a piece of string around it. "I guess that'll do," he said.

"Thank you!" said Eddie. He gave the man his seventy-five cents.

Eddie decided to slip out the back door with his bundle. When he got to the car, he quickly opened the trunk. Then he set the box inside.

Eddie returned to the front steps just in time. When his father and mother came out, he was looking at a rusty old lock.

"Hey, look at the swell old lock!" called Eddie as if nothing had happened.

"It's a piece of junk!" said Mr. Wilson. "Put it down and come along, son!"

They all got into the car and drove off. Eddie sat in the front seat between his father and mother. For some time Eddie said nothing. Suddenly he said, "Well, I had a very enjoyable day today."

Mr. Wilson stopped the car with a loud screech. Slowly he turned around and looked on the back seat. Nothing was there.

"What did you say, Eddie?" he asked as he started the car.

"I just said I had a very enjoyable day today," Eddie replied.

Again Mr. Wilson stopped the car with a screech. Then he got out and opened the trunk. There was Eddie's box.

"Please, Dad!" Eddie begged before Mr. Wilson could open the box. "That isn't junk. It's valuable antique property."

"Eddie," said his father, "no more junk, and I mean it!" He carried Eddie's box to a rubbish can on the street.

As he set the box down, Mr. Wilson saw the end of the carriage lamp. He took off the string and opened the box.

"Say!" Mr. Wilson said. "This could be a good carriage lamp! A little oil polish will make this rusty lamp shiny. Then I'll set it on that post by the door."

"But I bought it, Dad," said Eddie. "I gave a quarter for it."

"Well, I'll give you a dollar for it, son," said his father. "How is that?"

"Okay," said Eddie.

"Look, Mother!" Mr. Wilson said. "Look at this carriage lamp."

Mrs. Wilson was looking inside Eddie's box, too. "Why, look at this old coffee grinder!" she said. "Oh, I want this! A little red paint is all it needs. It'll make a beautiful antique lamp!"

"But I bought it, Mom," said Eddie. "I gave my quarters for it."

"I'll give you a dollar for it," she said. "Is a dollar all right?"

"Oh, Mom!" said Eddie. "I like the swell wheels on that old coffee grinder."

"Well, then I'll give you two dollars for it," said his mother. "Two dollars is a lot of money, Eddie."

"Okay," Eddie said.

Later, as they drove home, Eddie said, "Dad, guess what I'm going to do when I grow up. I'm going to sell junk! I can make a lot of money selling junk."

27

"You sure can!" said Mr. Wilson. "How about us selling junk together?"

"Okay, Dad," said Eddie. "Will we have a shop of our own?"

"Certainly!" said Eddie's father. "And we'll have a big sign that says WILSON AND SON—ALL KINDS OF JUNK."

Think about This:

1 What is the difference between junk and antiques?
2 What do you think Eddie's father did with the telephone pole that Eddie brought home?
3 Why do you suppose Eddie and his father think that they can make money selling antiques?

song   streams   dimes

young   yesterday   yelling

eager   goat   gulped   jiggled

grocery   faces   cell   bounced

tops   mats   pink   fed

puff   nanny   pulls

slam

yelping

Gus

twice

slid

yelled

Jenkin

Gus'll

terrible-tempered

Terrible-tempered Goose

The Chase

Gus was a goose. He was sleek and white and terrible-tempered! He chased anyone who came near him. But still Dan Jenkin was proud of Gus.

"Dad, may I show Gus at the fair?" asked Dan one day.

Mr. Jenkin thought about that. He was already taking his two cows, Cindy's lamb, Mother's pickles, and Aunt Hattie's quilt. Now Dan wanted his terrible-tempered goose to go to the fair, too.

"All right, you may take him," sighed Mr. Jenkin. "But you'll have to get Gus into a crate yourself."

Dan thought about that. He would have to get the goose up from the pond. And the only sure way to do that was to get Gus to chase someone. Someone like Cindy!

Dan asked Cindy to let Gus chase her. But Gus had chased her before. "No!" yelled Cindy. "He can't chase me! That goose is mean! Mean!"

"All you have to do," said Dan, "is get his attention. It'll be easy. Gus'll chase you up from the pond, and I'll catch him in a crate when he gets here."

"If it's so easy, let that mean goose chase you," said Cindy. "I'll catch him in the crate."

Dan knew better than to ask Cindy twice. She was terrified of Gus.

Dan found a rusty old wire crate. Then he carried it to the back gate. "You sit on the fence and hold the crate door open with this string," he told Cindy. "Then Gus'll chase me from the pond to the gate. I'll jump over the crate, and Gus'll run inside it. Then you let the door slam shut."

Twice they tried the plan without Gus. It seemed to work, so Dan went to the pond.

"Gus! Hey, Gus!" called Dan. He yelled and waved to get his attention.

With a honk Gus started off across the pasture after Dan. The race was on.

Dan stayed ahead until he slid and landed in the mud. Then he really had to run. That fierce honk was right behind him!

Just as Dan got near the fence, his dog, Blackie, ran a little ahead and sniffed at the crate. Then he stretched his legs and crawled inside.

"Get out, Blackie! Get!" cried Cindy.

But it was too late. Dan jumped over the crate just fine. But then he slid against the fence so hard that he knocked Cindy off into the mud. The string dropped, and the door closed with Blackie shut inside. Gus banged his head into the closed door. This made him even more angry.

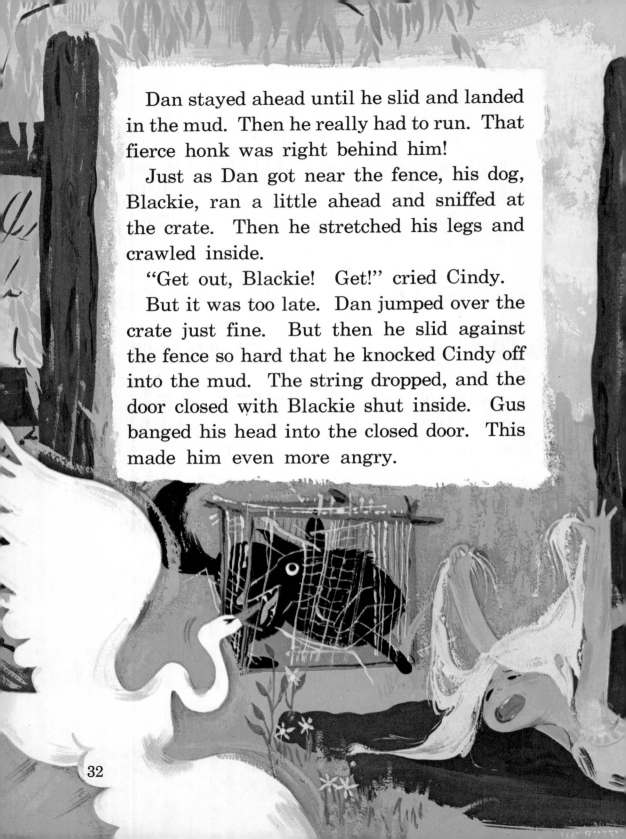

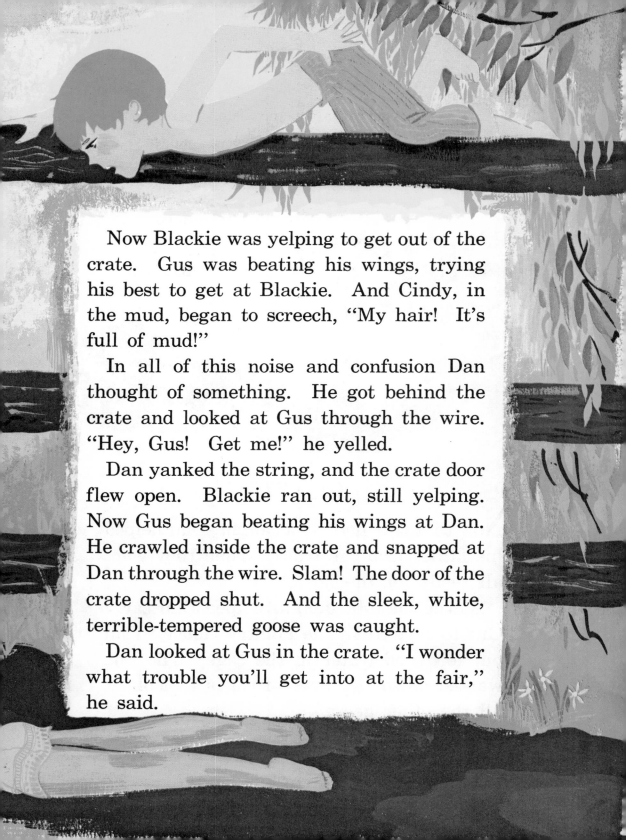

Now Blackie was yelping to get out of the crate. Gus was beating his wings, trying his best to get at Blackie. And Cindy, in the mud, began to screech, "My hair! It's full of mud!"

In all of this noise and confusion Dan thought of something. He got behind the crate and looked at Gus through the wire. "Hey, Gus! Get me!" he yelled.

Dan yanked the string, and the crate door flew open. Blackie ran out, still yelping. Now Gus began beating his wings at Dan. He crawled inside the crate and snapped at Dan through the wire. Slam! The door of the crate dropped shut. And the sleek, white, terrible-tempered goose was caught.

Dan looked at Gus in the crate. "I wonder what trouble you'll get into at the fair," he said.

trained alive needle

bulge hedge budge

lick flash pant struck

prize

judges

Dan's

swallowed

ribbon

poultry

Bascomb

Cage 37

Now that Gus had been caught, Dan helped his father load the truck. Then they were all ready for the fair.

At the fair Mr. Jenkin helped Dan carry Gus to cage 37 in the Poultry House. Dan put feed and water in the cage. Then he walked down the rows of cages to look at all the other geese.

Dan swallowed hard when he got back to Gus. "You may not win first prize for being the best," he said. "But if they give a prize for being the meanest, you're sure to win it!"

The next day was important for Cindy and Dan. It was the day that the judges gave out ribbons. The Jenkin family planned to meet in front of the Poultry House when the judges were through.

Mr. Jenkin's cows won blue ribbons, as they did each year. Mrs. Jenkin's pickles tied for second place. And the judge gave Aunt Hattie's quilt first prize. The family had done well this year, so far.

"Maybe Cindy's lamb and Dan's goose won ribbons," said Mother.

The family found Cindy beside her lamb, brushing its soft wool with her fingers. Sure enough, a long white ribbon for third place was tied around its neck.

But when the Jenkins got to Gus, there was no ribbon. Not a red ribbon for second place. Not even a white one for third. No ribbon at all.

"I hope Dan won't be sad," said Mother.

They went around to all the cages to find the goose with the blue ribbon. They found the red ribbon for second place and other cages with white ribbons for third place. But no one found the blue ribbon.

Just then Dan came up. "I spent my money on the rides," he said. Then he looked at cage 37. "Poor Gus! He didn't win, did he?" said Dan.

"It's very strange," said Mr. Jenkin. "We didn't find the goose with the blue ribbon. Maybe Mr. Bascomb, the poultry judge, can tell us which one has it."

The Jenkins found Mr. Bascomb standing just outside the Poultry House. Mr. Bascomb opened his record book. He ran his fingers down the rows on the page. "Here it is," he said. "Number 37."

That was Gus!

"I knew it!" cried Dan. "Gus is the best goose at the fair!"

Mr. Bascomb and the Jenkins hurried to number 37. Dan tried to pat Gus. But Gus snapped at his fingers.

"But where is the blue ribbon?" asked Mr. Jenkin.

"Maybe it fell off," said Mr. Bascomb. "Here, I have an extra one." He took a blue ribbon out of his record book and tied it to the cage.

Suddenly Gus stuck his beak through the wire, caught the ribbon, and shook it. Then he swallowed it!

"Well, now!" cried Mr. Bascomb. "So you swallowed the other ribbon, too. Here, I'll give my last extra ribbon to Dan!"

The rest of the day Dan stood inside the Poultry House shouting, "Meanest goose that ever lived!" And when anyone stopped, Dan pointed to Gus and said, "He's the only animal here to win three blue ribbons. Two to eat, and one to keep!"

We work with words.

eye buckeye eyelid
though trough ghoul ghastly
notice favorite practice
smokestack railroad blindfold
clippers cleaned claws
crowd creak crashed
screeched scramble screamed
praised pretzel pricked

Sight words.

yeah echoed José whom

Sound the words.

eyeholes
ghosts
practiced
slowpoke
clapping
creaky
scrambled
probably
scary
agreed

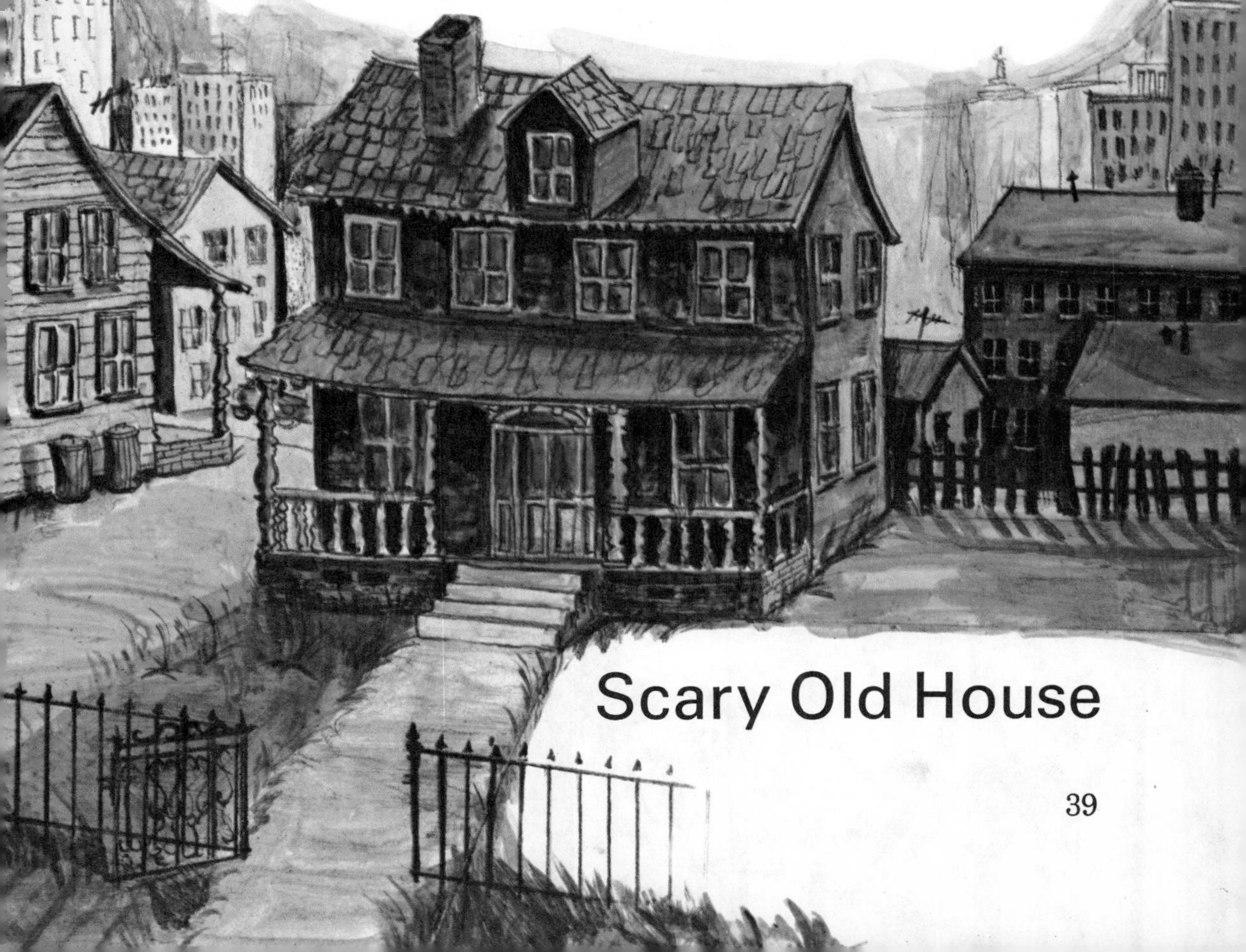

Scary Old House

José called up the stairs to Bill. "Hey, let's get out of this spooky house. It's getting dark."

Creak, creak, creak! Bang! Noises came from the top of the stairs, and a voice said, "Ooo-oo! Eee-ee! I'm a ghost. I'm coming to get you!"

"Come on, Bill," José called again. "You don't scare me. But it's getting dark, and I have to go home."

Bill came down the stairs. He and José crept out the door. As they went through the gate, they turned back. The old house looked dark and spooky, just the way the boys liked it.

Suddenly José heard a dog bark. He nudged Bill and pointed up the street. "Look at the size of that dog!" he whispered. "It must be the one I heard barking. But who's that boy with the dog?"

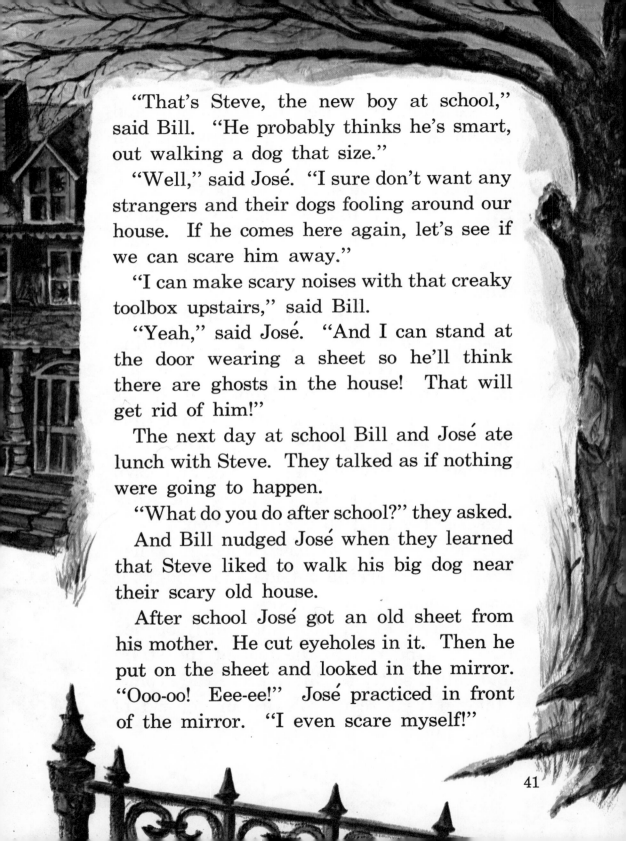

"That's Steve, the new boy at school," said Bill. "He probably thinks he's smart, out walking a dog that size."

"Well," said José. "I sure don't want any strangers and their dogs fooling around our house. If he comes here again, let's see if we can scare him away."

"I can make scary noises with that creaky toolbox upstairs," said Bill.

"Yeah," said José. "And I can stand at the door wearing a sheet so he'll think there are ghosts in the house! That will get rid of him!"

The next day at school Bill and José ate lunch with Steve. They talked as if nothing were going to happen.

"What do you do after school?" they asked.

And Bill nudged José when they learned that Steve liked to walk his big dog near their scary old house.

After school José got an old sheet from his mother. He cut eyeholes in it. Then he put on the sheet and looked in the mirror. "Ooo-oo! Eee-ee!" José practiced in front of the mirror. "I even scare myself!"

41

José stuck the sheet under his arm and ran to the old house. Bill was waiting on the front steps.

"What took you so long, slowpoke?" asked Bill. "I don't like waiting here alone."

"I practiced being a spooky ghost," said José. "Besides, I got here before Steve, didn't I?"

The two boys went inside. Then Bill went upstairs and practiced opening and shutting the creaky toolbox. Creak, creak, creak! Bang! Then he started clapping his hands to make even more noise. At the same time José practiced being a spooky ghost downstairs. He waved his arms up and down and moaned, "Ooo-oo! Eee-ee!" The scary noises echoed all through the house.

Suddenly the two boys stopped. They heard a dog barking outside and thought it was probably Steve's dog.

José crept to the door and slowly opened it. Then he ran to the foot of the stairs and called softly to Bill, "Here they come! Make it real scary so we can get rid of them quick!"

A moment later Steve and his big dog
came by the old house. José crept from
behind the front door and started waving his
arms. Creak, creak, creak! Bang! Scary
noises came from the house. "Ooo-oo!
Eeee-ee!" moaned José. "I'm a ghost. And
I'm coming to get you."

"Hi, José," said Steve. "Why in the world
are you wearing that sheet?"

Behind the eyeholes, José's eyes grew
wide in surprise. "I'm a scary ghost!" he
said as he crept a little closer.

"Don't be silly," said Steve. "I know it's
you. You can't scare me."

José walked out to the gate. "How did you
know it was me?" he asked.

"I'd know your cowboy boots anywhere,"
he said. "I saw them when you were waving
your arms and clumping around."

"Aw!" said José. "We were trying to scare you."

"We?" asked Steve. "Is Bill here, too?"

Just that moment more creaky noises came from the house. Cr-reak, cr-reak, cr-reak! Bang! Steve's dog started barking.

"That's Bill making the noise. He's just fooling around, shutting a creaky toolbox. Come on inside."

José took off the sheet and threw it on the front steps. Steve closed the gate and let his dog run in the yard.

Inside, José yelled to Bill. "Come on down. Steve isn't scared of ghosts."

Bill looked a little red as he came down the stairs. Then all at once he pointed to the front door. His red face was now as white as a ghost.

"L-look!" Bill cried. "Th-that ghost is coming in here!"

The boys stared at the sheet moving into the house. Cr-reak, cr-reak! Noises came from under the sheet. Bill ran down the stairs and fell over José. "Quick! The back door!" he shouted.

The two boys ran to the back door and pushed and pulled to get it open. But the door was stuck.

"Come and help, Steve!" shouted Bill. "Help get this door open!"

But Steve didn't come. Slowly the sheet moved closer and closer as it followed the boys to the door.

"The window! The window!" yelled José. "Head for the window!"

The boys scrambled past the sheet to the window. They pushed and banged, trying to open it. The window was stuck, too.

"Help us, Steve! Don't just stand there!" cried José.

But Steve did just stand there. He was watching as the sheet swayed and wiggled closer to the boys.

45

"The stairs! Up the stairs, slowpoke!"
Bill yelled to José.

José and Bill scrambled up the stairs,
pushing each other as they went. And the
sound of José's cowboy boots echoed through
the house.

Suddenly Steve started clapping his hands
and laughing. Then he gave a whistle.

The sheet stopped. It turned away from
the stairs and wiggled up to Steve. The two
boys watched from the top of the stairs,
their faces as white as ghost faces.

Steve picked up the sheet. "It's my dog!"
he laughed. "He didn't mean to scare you."

As the boys came slowly down the stairs,
they began to laugh, too. Soon their faces
were red from laughing.

At last Bill said, "This old house is my dad's. If you'll bring your dog, we can make this scary old house a fun house every day after school."

The big dog barked and ran out the door. "All right," said Steve, "but there's just one thing. Let's make a deal not to scare each other again—ever. Agreed?"

"Agreed!" echoed José and Bill. "It's a deal!"

Think about This:

1 What breed do you think Steve's dog is? Do you think the author should have told you what kind it is? Why?
2 Have you ever tried to scare anyone? Were you more frightened than the person whom you tried to scare? How did it happen?
3 If these three boys were in your club, which would you choose as its leader?

Shivers

Oh, why didn't I start home earlier?
Now it is dark and spooky,
And the old house is in front of me.
A hinge breaks, a shutter falls.
Why did that have to happen now?
A little drip, and another,
Then another coming from some gutter.
A leaf falls right in front of me,
An owl hoots.
I look back, then I hear a meow.
I turn and run!
Don't look back!

The warmth and glow of home
Makes me feel warm inside.

by Jim DeYoung, Age 9

48

tests stuff stall steep

he'd what'll aren't

straw strokes strapped

flames flash floating

scurrying scattered scold

tongue

stalling

shouldn't

streams

flap

scowl

eye

Henry

bald

fellows

clippers

canine

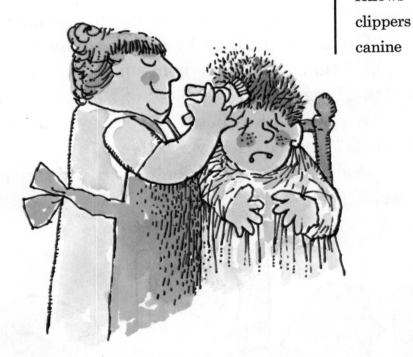

Henry Uses His Head

49

One night Henry wore his sailor hat to the dinner table. His mother looked at him, then at his father, and sighed.

"You're looking pretty gloomy," said Mr. Huggins as he filled Henry's plate.

"Yeah," said Henry. "Don't give me much. I'm not very hungry." Henry couldn't take any chances with his upper loose teeth, one on either side of his grown-up front teeth. He had to have them to show off to people who started making fun of his hair.

"I'm afraid the boys have been giving him a bad time about his home haircut," said Mrs. Huggins.

"Would you feel better if you went to the barber?" asked Henry's father.

"Well, maybe, but I don't think anything would help very much," said Henry.

"I wonder if—" began Mrs. Huggins. Then she stopped and suddenly smiled at Henry.

Henry wiggled his teeth and wondered what his mother was planning. He hoped it wasn't anything about another haircut.

"Really, Henry," said his mother, "you shouldn't flap your teeth that way."

"Aw, Mom, they don't flap," said Henry. "They just wiggle."

"I read that the cost of living has gone up, so old teeth left under a pillow are now turning into quarters, not dimes," said Mr. Huggins. Henry grinned. He knew it was really his father who always left the dimes. But now, much as he could use two quarters, he needed two loose teeth more.

The next morning Henry couldn't see that his hair had grown any, so he put on his sailor hat. He followed his dog, Ribsy, out the door and sat down on the front steps. Henry couldn't keep from pushing first his right tooth, then his left tooth, with his tongue. These two teeth were called canine teeth because they were pointed like the teeth of a dog.

Henry happened to look up. Thinking he must be seeing things, he jumped up and stared. Robert and Scooter were walking toward him, both of them wearing sailor hats turned down over their ears.

"How do you like that? Wearing sailor hats to make fun of me," thought Henry.

Side by side the two boys walked past the house. They did not seem to see Henry.

Henry stared. "What's wrong with them?" he wondered. Then a thought struck Henry. Could it be? Suddenly he had a feeling that he wasn't the only boy with a chewed-up haircut. "Hey!" he yelled.

But Robert and Scooter walked on.

Henry had to know for sure. If he wasn't the only one with chewed-up hair, things wouldn't be so bad.

"Hey, fellows!" he yelled. As he yelled, his tongue hit one of his loose teeth. And that gave him an idea. "Want to watch me pull my teeth?"

The boys stopped and turned around.

"I have a new way to pull them," called Henry, trying hard to think of a way.

"How?" asked Scooter as he and Robert came up the steps.

"You'll see," said Henry. To stall for time, he began fishing through his pockets and found a piece of string.

He couldn't let the boys get away until he found out what had happened. "Say—how come you fellows are wearing hats? Did you get your hair cut?" he asked.

"We sure did," said Scooter. "And it's all your fault."

"What do you mean, it's all my fault?" asked Henry. "What did I do?"

"You know," Scooter said with a scowl. "If you ask me, it was a mean trick."

"What was a mean trick?" Henry asked. "What are you talking about?"

"Your mother told our mothers about the sale on hair clippers," said Scooter. "She called them just like you told her to. And they both went right over to the sale and bought clippers."

"My mother?" Henry was really surprised. "My mother called your mothers?"

"Didn't you know?" Robert asked.

"No," said Henry. "Cross my heart and hope to die."

Well, so that was what his mother had been planning last night! Henry wanted to laugh, but he didn't.

"See?" said Robert to Scooter. "I told you it wasn't his idea."

Henry looked hurt. "You're some friend, thinking I'd do a mean thing like that."

"Well, maybe you didn't," said Scooter, "but I bet you haven't really thought of a way to pull your teeth."

"I have, too," said Henry. He wondered how he was going to get out of this. He slowly tied one end of the string to his right tooth. Then he slowly tied the other end of the string to his left tooth while he tried to think of a way to stall. "How about letting me look at your hair?"

"Come on! Let's see you pull your teeth," said Scooter.

"I need more string," explained Henry.

Both the boys looked in their pockets. "I don't have any," said Robert.

"I don't either," said Scooter. "You're just stalling."

"I'm not either stalling." Then suddenly Henry had an idea. And all he needed was a little help from Ribsy.

Henry picked up Ribsy's tug-of-war rope. He tied one end to the middle of the string that was around his two teeth and threw the other end into the grass. "Here, Ribsy," Henry called.

Ribsy opened one eye and looked at Henry. He opened the other eye and came running across the grass. "Wuf!" he said.

Ribsy grabbed the end of the rope and pulled hard. Henry's teeth flew out of his mouth so fast he didn't even feel them go. Henry poked his tongue into the holes that were left. "How's that for a way to pull teeth?" he asked.

"Say, that was smart!" Robert cried. "I never heard of anyone having a dog pull his teeth before."

"A tooth-pulling dog. That's pretty good!" said Scooter.

"Good old Ribsy," said Henry, and hugged him. "He's a smart dog."

57

Henry put his teeth into his pocket so that he could put them under his pillow that night. Then he looked at Robert and Scooter, who still had on their sailor hats. "Well, how about letting me see your hair?" he asked, pulling off his own hat.

"No!" Scooter yelled and held his hat down over his ears.

"Aw, come on," said Henry. "I pulled my teeth like I said I would."

Robert took off his hat, and he and Henry looked at each other's haircuts. "Yours is better in front, but mine is better in back," Robert said. "But we're better off than Scooter. He's bald on one side."

"No joke?" said Henry. "Really bald?" Then he and Robert began to laugh.

Scooter looked even more gloomy. "It's all right for you fellows to laugh. You're in the same room at school and can stick together. But I'm all by myself."

"Gee, that's rough," said Robert. But he and Henry didn't look very sorry.

Then Henry had another idea. "Hey, look, fellows," he said. He filled his mouth from the garden hose and blew. Two streams of water shot through the gaps in his teeth. Boy, oh boy! He still had something to show the kids at school. Something besides his haircut.

FOOTPRINTS

spray   roadway   bray

sway

dye   buy   lye

good-bye

breaking   instead   meant   beamed

eager

collie   Susie   Janie

Frannie

bravest   brief   brakes

breath

cell   burrs   alley   stuff

Puff

shed   path   cocked

sings

soundproof

canary   Lisa

apiece

Lisa's Song

When Mother asked Lisa what she wanted for her birthday, Lisa answered her very quickly.

"One of Mrs. Puff's canaries!" And then she added, "If a canary doesn't cost too awfully much."

Mrs. Puff's canaries sold for six dollars apiece. Lisa knew six dollars could buy many things her family needed. So Mother might not be able to spend that much for Lisa's birthday.

Mother smiled. "I don't think six dollars is too much. Stop by Mrs. Puff's and choose the canary you want," she said.

The next day after school, feeling very excited, Lisa ran straight to Mrs. Puff's apartment. Mrs. Puff led her right to the room where the canary cages hung.

Lisa's eager eyes beamed as she looked around. "I don't see Frannie!" she said.

"Frannie? Oh, I put him in my room in a cage by himself," said Mrs. Puff.

Lisa laughed. "You probably hid Frannie in your room because you knew I'd choose him," she said.

"I'm afraid you can't take Frannie," said
Mrs. Puff. Then she went to a large cage
which hung by the window. She whistled a
little song. One small yellow bird in the
cage began to sway and sing. And the
others followed along.

Mrs. Puff said kindly to Lisa, "Wouldn't
you like one of these instead?"

Lisa was silent. It seemed to her that
birds were just like people—each one was
different. She wanted Frannie, with his
dark green coat. Frannie would just sway in
his swing until she came to see him. Then
he would always take a deep breath and sing
a sweet song just for her.

"I understand why you're so upset," said Mrs. Puff, "and I'm sorry. But you see, I plan to take Frannie to a music school. People often pay as much as seventy-five to a hundred dollars apiece for special birds like Frannie."

Lisa turned away. "Thank you," she said in a soft voice. "Then I guess I don't want a canary right now."

"Would you like to go along when I take Frannie to music school next Saturday?" asked Mrs. Puff.

Lisa nodded. "Good-bye," she said.

Early on Saturday morning Mrs. Puff and Lisa drove to the Voice Training School for Canaries. Lisa held Frannie's small covered cage on her lap. She was eager now to meet Frannie's teacher.

While they were waiting for the teacher, Mrs. Puff showed Lisa around. In one room they found many large cages. There were ten yellow canaries in each cage.

"See the signs on the doors of the cages? They tell about the birds inside," said Mrs. Puff.

"Will Frannie's cage be hung in here?" asked Lisa.

"Oh, no," said Mrs. Puff. "The special birds are in a room with a glass door. Each one is kept in a soundproof cage."

"Why are they kept in soundproof cages?" she asked.

"Because canaries have such good ears," said Mrs. Puff. "They learn to sing any sound they hear, even when they are babies. But the teacher wants these birds to learn just one beautiful song, so she keeps them in soundproof cages. Every day the teacher lets each bird hear the same song played on a record. As soon as the bird has learned the song, he is ready to be sold. He is valuable because he can sing a beautiful song."

Lisa's thoughts wandered back to Frannie. He wouldn't like living without anyone else around. It would be such a lonely life for a little bird. Lisa had wanted to put his cage in her room where he could sway and sing. Later she would have bought another little canary so Frannie wouldn't have to live all alone.

At last the teacher came to the waiting room. "Bring your birds in, please," she said to Mrs. Puff.

"I have just one bird for your training class today," said Mrs. Puff. And she took the cover off Frannie's cage.

Inside, Frannie sat very still and sad. Lisa went over to tell him good-bye. The green canary lifted his head and took a deep breath. Then his song for Lisa rolled out just as it always did.

"How very beautiful!" said the teacher. "How old is he?"

"Six months," said Mrs. Puff.

"That's a little old for our class," the teacher explained. "But we will keep him for a week. Then I can tell you more. We'll want to buy him, I'm sure."

Lisa was silent on the way home.

"Just think, Lisa," said Mrs. Puff. "Many important people have birds from the music school. Frannie may even go to live at the White House!"

Mrs. Puff was trying to make Lisa feel better. But it didn't help at all.

The next Saturday was Lisa's birthday. She worked around the house in the morning. That afternoon she just sat in her room, thinking about Frannie's lonely life.

"Lisa!" called her mother.

Lisa walked to the living room. There sat Mrs. Puff with a cage on her lap.

Mrs. Puff said, "Happy birthday, Lisa. It's the one you chose."

Lisa dropped beside the cage. She could not get the cover off fast enough.

"Frannie! Oh, it's really you!" cried the surprised Lisa.

Frannie lifted his head. He took a deep breath and opened his small beak. Then he sang his beautiful song.

"There it is!" said Mrs. Puff. "Frannie wouldn't sing it in music class, but he sings it for Lisa."

Lisa's eyes beamed. "It's Lisa's song!" she said.

Think about This:

1 Signs were on each cage at the Voice Training School for Canaries. If Lisa made a sign for Frannie's cage, what do you think she would write on it?
2 Lisa thought birds were much like people. Can you think of some ways that birds are like people?

we'd   he'd   you'd

they'd

schoolhouse   scheme   schooner

Schooner's

smoking   smoldering   smaller

smashed

swished   swoop   swung

swarming

phone   phony   trophy

Murphy

scrap   scrub   screeched

screamed

Jerry

squad   Sergeant

vegetables

Susie

Trouble with Susie

69

Calling All Cars

One day Jerry was out looking for Susie when he heard the loud noise of a police car. He watched it as it screamed by. He really didn't think much about it until he heard a second police car.

"Sure hope they're not after Susie," he thought.

A third police car shot past Jerry. It made such a loud screech it hurt his ears. Then two more screamed by, their red lights flashing. All the squad cars were headed down Third Street.

Jerry heard a voice from one of the squad cars say, "Calling all cars. A robber is breaking into Schooner's Grocery."

Jerry knew where Schooner's Grocery was.
So he ran to see if the robber was still
there. But what he saw was Mr. Schooner's
glass window smashed in. Vegetables were
scattered all over the sidewalk.

The police were swarming out of their
squad cars and rushing toward the store.
They ran up the alley along one side of
Schooner's. Then, just as they came around
the building, another window broke.

That's when Jerry saw Susie. There she
stood, outside that second smashed window
at Schooner's.

"Look at that!" Sergeant Murphy cried.
"It's a billy goat! Sure as I'm alive, it's
a hardheaded billy goat!"

71

"Nanny goat," Jerry thought. But Jerry couldn't tell the sergeant just now. Susie stood in front of the flashing lights a second. Then she grabbed a head of lettuce from the smashed window and ran.

"After the goat, men!" Sergeant Murphy cried. "He took a head of lettuce!"

All the police came swarming after Susie. They scattered down the alley and in every direction so she couldn't get away.

Jerry ran hard, trying to keep up. But the goat and the policemen left him far behind. There was nothing he could do for Susie now.

"Poor Susie can run fast," thought Jerry. "But those policemen will be too much for her. They'll chase her into a corner, and she won't be able to get away."

Jerry wondered what they'd do to a goat for breaking store windows and taking fresh vegetables. What if the police had been ordered to take Susie "dead or alive"? He wondered if all this running would be good for Susie. Would she be frightened? Poor nanny goat!

Jerry didn't have long to wonder. Soon the squad cars returned with Susie. She went by, riding in the back seat between two large policemen.

Jerry tried to stop them, but he was too far away. No one seemed to see him. All the police were in their squad cars, riding toward the station. Soon they were gone.

Now there was nothing for Jerry to do but run after the squad cars. What were the police going to do? Jerry had to get to the station fast!

Think about This:

1 What would you do with Susie if you were one of the policemen?

73

claws　clever　cleaned

least　spreading　greater　easier

neighbor's　Jo's　lady's

pricked　pretend　proof

crowd　cracky　crossing

office　central　medicine

change

claim

bleat

Jerry's

private

crashed

cell

continued

several

mention

Behind Bars

Jerry was out of breath by the time he reached the police station. But he went straight inside and hurried right up to Sergeant Murphy.

"I came to get my goat," Jerry said. He tried to sound as rough as he could.

Sergeant Murphy looked up from his desk and frowned.

"Your goat!" he cried. "You claim that's your goat that broke into Mr. Schooner's grocery on Third Street?"

"Y-yes, sir," Jerry answered.

Now several policemen in the room crowded around Jerry and the sergeant. Jerry tried to keep back his tears.

"Son," Sergeant Murphy began, "you may wish to change your mind when you hear what that goat has done." He took out the police record and began to read, "One billy goat charged with breaking two large windows, taking private property, and running from the police, just to mention a few things in this record."

Sergeant Murphy closed the record book. "Let me finish, son," he continued. "It took five squad cars and ten policemen to capture that goat. Why, he could have torn up half the city! Are you sure you want to claim him?"

"Yes, sir," Jerry replied. Several times he had wanted to tell Sergeant Murphy that Susie wasn't a billy goat. But Jerry was so scared he could hardly talk.

"Let's go to the jail," said Sergeant Murphy. "We'll find out if you're really the owner of that goat." At hearing this, several policemen closed in and walked just behind Jerry.

Susie was in jail, all right. Everyone watched as she ate the hay that had been put in her own private cell. Or at least they thought it was private. But suddenly a small bleat came from one corner of the cell. There on the hay was a baby goat, so wobbly it could hardly stand up!

"Two goats!" the sergeant shouted. "That billy goat we caught had a baby! Sure as I'm alive, that's no billy goat!"

"Susie is a nanny goat," Jerry said. "I could have told you if you had let me. Now I'll claim both Susie and her baby and take them home."

"Hold on," said Sergeant Murphy. "That bill for Schooner's windows and all those vegetables hasn't been paid. Someone has to pay that bill before we can let this goat go home."

Tears came to Jerry's eyes. He had no money of his own, and his dad wouldn't be home until late tomorrow. He couldn't leave Susie and her new baby in jail all night. He just couldn't!

"Look," Jerry said, "you've got to obey the law, too, don't you?"

"Certainly," replied the sergeant.

"Then how is it that you can keep two goats in jail when you caught only one?" Jerry asked.

The policemen looked at each other.

"You're right," said the sergeant. "The little goat hasn't crashed into anything. It has done nothing against the law. You may take it home."

Jerry continued, "Your record also says that you caught a billy goat. So you can't keep a nanny goat."

"Now, look here, son," Sergeant Murphy said. "This goat is charged with breaking Mr. Schooner's windows and taking a head of lettuce, not to mention the vegetables he scattered. We'll just change the word *billy* to *nanny* in the record book."

Jerry didn't know what to do. No one here understood. Sergeant Murphy lifted the baby goat to Jerry's arms and showed them out the door.

Now Susie had been silent from the start to the finish of this deal. But not now! She could hardly just stand by and let her baby leave without her.

Susie let out a loud bleat. She charged right into the cell door and crashed it wide open. She ran right past the police and shot straight toward the door. Out she went after her baby.

When Susie caught up with Jerry, he heard several policemen shouting. He was afraid the police had chased after Susie again. But instead the police cheered and waved good-bye! Now Jerry knew they were glad to be rid of the goats. They probably knew he would bring the money to pay for those two windows tomorrow.

Jerry carried the wobbly new baby for Susie. Together the three went home.

An Introduction to Dogs

The dog is man's best friend.
He has a tail on one end.
Up in front he has teeth.
And four legs underneath.

Dogs like to bark.
They like it best after dark.
They not only frighten prowlers away
But also hold the sandman at bay.

A dog that is indoors
To be let out implores.
You let him out and what then?
He wants back in again.

Dogs display reluctance and wrath
If you try to give them a bath.
They bury bones in hideaways
And half the time they trot sideaways.

They cheer up people who are frowning,
And rescue people who are drowning,
They also track mud on beds,
And chew people's clothes to shreds.

Dogs in the country have fun.
They run and run and run.
But in the city this species
Is dragged around on leashes.

Dogs are upright as a steeple
And much more loyal than people.

by Ogden Nash

chin   touch   cherry

young   songs   springs   wringing

shaky   flash   bushel   shed

dragged   drawing   drew   dream

prairie   Bonnie   brownie

lick   stuff   blank   gum

actor   motor   beggar

invent   clever   currents

skid   skim   sketch

Sound the words.

porch

belonged

shaggy

Driscoll

collie

blast

collar

command

skirt

wherever

heel

Fogarty

Stanley

Sight word.

Suki

Suki Saddler and Her Dog

Suki Saddler and Ann Driscoll just didn't get along. And their dogs didn't, either. Oh, their dogs didn't fight, but they did snap at each other when they had the chance. Suki and Ann snapped at each other, too, but with words, not their teeth.

Suki was sure her dog, Fogarty, was the bravest dog in the world, but she didn't really know why. He was just a big, shaggy dog that was never in a hurry to get anywhere. Suki was forever saying, "Hurry, Fogarty!" or "Come on, Fogarty! Let's go!" But Fogarty paid no attention at all. He always poked along, sniffing a tree here, a rock there.

Ann Driscoll's dog, Jo Jo, was different from Fogarty in almost every way. He never poked along. He bounced along behind Ann wherever she went. Sometimes Ann would say, "Heel!" and Jo Jo would follow her command. But this was not the only command Jo Jo would follow. When Ann said, "Blast," Jo Jo would bark twice and run home, where he would wait for Ann on the front porch.

Almost every day Ann walked Jo Jo by Suki's house. Suki was certain that Ann did it to make her angry. This day was no different from the others. Suki and Fogarty sat on the front porch and watched Ann and her dog walk up the sidewalk.

"Hey, Suki!" Ann called. "Want to see Jo Jo's new trick?"

"Not very much," Suki answered as she picked up a small ball and bounced it across the grass. "Get it, Fogarty. Go get it," she said. Fogarty slowly got to his feet, took three steps after the ball, and then changed his mind.

"Ha! If that dog belonged to me, I'd trade him in on a collie like Jo Jo," Ann said. "Watch Jo Jo. Sit, Jo Jo. Sit." Jo Jo sat and waved a paw in the air.

"That's simple," Suki said. "Anyway, I've seen him do that before."

"Well," Ann snapped, "Jo Jo has a new trick. Just watch this." Jo Jo looked up at her. "Shake, Jo Jo." Jo Jo lifted one paw and waited for Ann to shake it. "Good dog," Ann said, and then looked at Suki. "Well?"

"That's pretty good, I guess," Suki said after a minute. Then she added, "For a collie." She got up and walked over to the front door. "I've got things to do. Come on, Fogarty." It took Fogarty a while to make up his mind, but at last he followed Suki through the front door.

Once inside the house, Suki turned to Fogarty. "Why don't you learn a trick? Sit, Fogarty. Sit." Fogarty cocked his head to one side and looked up at Suki. But he didn't sit. "Lie down, Fogarty. Lie down!" Suki ordered. Fogarty sat and began to scratch at his collar. "Oh, Fogarty!" Suki cried. "I guess you'll never be the smartest dog around, but I still think you're the best. Let's get the leash and go to the park."

On the way to the park, they passed a crowd of people waiting at the bus stop. Suki wanted to go on. But Fogarty decided that it was time to rest. So he dropped down on the sidewalk and closed his eyes. "Oh, Fogarty," Suki said.

A bus rolled up, screeched its brakes, and picked up the crowd of people. With a roar it left. Still Fogarty didn't get up. "Come on, Fogarty. Let's go," Suki said as she pulled on his leash. Slowly Fogarty got to his feet, shook himself all over, and stretched. Then he turned and looked back down the sidewalk. Suki looked, too. "Oh, no!" she said. "Not them." There was Ann with her collie, Jo Jo.

Suki and Fogarty walked to the signal light at the corner. It was red. By the time it turned green, Ann and Jo Jo had caught up with them.

When they reached the park, Suki turned to Ann and said, "Did you follow us?"

"Why should I want to follow you?" Ann answered. "I've got the smartest dog in town, and I've got a puppet that's as smart as some people I know." She held up a hand puppet with a long, red skirt. "I call him Stanley."

"Stanley? That's a funny name for a puppet," Suki said.

"I don't think so. I thought it up myself," Ann said. "Watch, I'll make him talk. He'll show you how smart he is."

Ann held the puppet and began to ask questions and then answer them in a deep voice as she moved the puppet up and down. Suki watched for a few minutes and then walked over by a small lake and took off Fogarty's leash.

"Hey," Ann called, "you're not watching." Then she ran toward Suki. Jo Jo ran along with her. But just a few feet from the lake, Jo Jo darted between her legs. Down she fell in the mud. Stanley, the puppet, flew off her hand and landed far out in the water.

"My puppet!" she cried. Then she looked at Jo Jo. "Go get Stanley, Jo Jo. Get him."

Jo Jo ran to the water and stopped. "Get him!" Ann ordered, but Jo Jo would not move.

Suki thought for a moment and then turned to Fogarty. "Get it, Fogarty. Go get it!" Fogarty cocked his head at Suki and then, with a great splash, jumped into the water. Slowly he moved toward the puppet. Just as it began to sink, he grabbed it by the skirt and brought it to the bank.

Ann picked up her wet puppet and looked at it for a long time. "Suki, I guess your dog is pretty smart after all."

Suki patted Fogarty on the head before she answered. "Well, he may not be the smartest dog in the world, but I think he's the bravest. Maybe he's just smart enough to know when to be smart."

"I think I'd better go on home now," Ann said. "Want to walk with me?"

"Sure," Suki answered. "Come on, Fogarty." But Fogarty was sound asleep under a tree, and Jo Jo was curled up next to him.

priest   thief   pieces

mild   hind   grind

trim   trained   trunks

washed   shade   trash

break   neat   steamed   heading

period

brief

blind

traffic

shepherd

easier

trainer

blindfold

difficult

commands

harness

More Than a Pet

Dogs make good pets because they like being with people. A pet dog can be like a best friend. He will do almost anything he can for someone he cares about.

But some dogs are more than just good pets. For thousands of years dogs have been working for people. Maybe you have heard about dogs being trained to care for sheep and other animals. You may have heard about dogs being trained to find lost children. And you probably know that some dogs are trained to guide blind people. These dogs are called Seeing Eye dogs.

A little over forty years ago the first Seeing Eye dog was trained to help a blind man. Now there are several hundred of these dogs at work all over the world.

Several different kinds of dogs have been trained to guide the blind. But the breed that seems to make the very best guide dog is the German shepherd. He does not seem to mind being out in the rain or snow. He is smart, strong, and easy to train. The German shepherd cares about blind people. He helps them walk from place to place.

Before a German shepherd becomes a Seeing Eye dog, he must go to a special training school for a period of about three months. The first lesson is brief. He learns to obey simple commands to sit or stay. When he has learned to make no mistakes with simple commands, he passes on to more difficult tests.

In his next period of training, the dog wears a special harness. He is taken to a city, and there he learns the rules of city traffic. His harness has a leash held by the trainer. The dog learns to guide his trainer safely as he passes through traffic in busy streets and crowds of people.

During these first three months, Seeing Eye dogs are trained by someone who can see. The dog has many things to learn. His trainer takes him through difficult tests. At the end of his training period, the dog is put through a final test. For this test, his trainer wears a blindfold. He holds the harness leash while the dog takes him safely across busy streets and through crowds of people.

When a dog has practiced and passed the test with his trainer wearing a blindfold, he is ready to help a blind person. His new owner may be a man, a woman, or even a child. It takes the dog and his blind master about a month to learn to work and live together.

During this brief month, the dog and his new owner stay together all the time. The dog sleeps in a room with his master and sits under the table when his master is eating. A trainer works with both the dog and master until they are ready to be on their own.

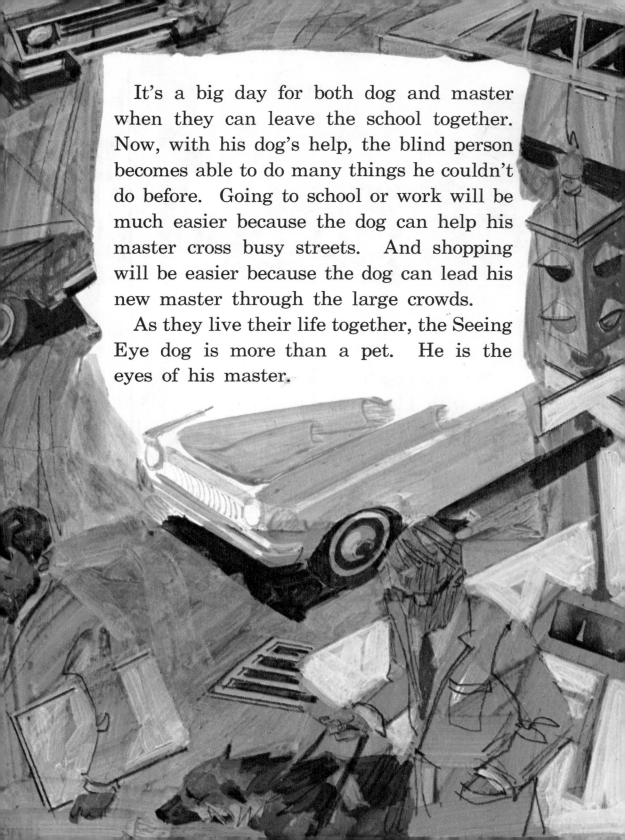

It's a big day for both dog and master when they can leave the school together. Now, with his dog's help, the blind person becomes able to do many things he couldn't do before. Going to school or work will be much easier because the dog can help his master cross busy streets. And shopping will be easier because the dog can lead his new master through the large crowds.

As they live their life together, the Seeing Eye dog is more than a pet. He is the eyes of his master.

path	thorny	earth	worth
bullet	pulls	butcher	bushel
office	noticed	promise	promised
gripped	grounds	groaned	Grumpy
spell	spilled	spots	speed

spotted

evening

Paula

Central

medicine

Lorenzo

nickered

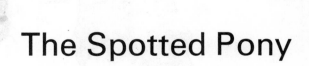

The Spotted Pony

One evening Leo went to the Central Pony Ride. He had been there many times. But this time he saw a new pony at the ride— a white pony with big brown spots.

Leo pulled some grass and brought it over to the pony ring. The spotted pony looked up at him with sad, dark eyes.

"You look awfully unhappy," Leo said to him. "And you're so thin!" The pony nibbled the grass Leo gave him and nickered softly at him.

Just then the owner of the Central Pony Ride came over to Leo. "Want to ride that spotted one?" he asked.

"Yes, I would like to," said Leo. "What's his name?"

"Grumpy," the man replied. "He won't eat, and he won't work."

Leo gave the man twenty-five cents and hopped up on Grumpy. The pony walked slowly around the path and came back to his place in the pony line. Then Leo slid off and gave Grumpy a quick pat. "Thanks, Grump," he said.

Early the next morning Leo went to the park once again. The man at Central Pony Ride was busy filling a tub with water. "Are you the same boy who rode Grumpy last night?" he asked.

Leo gulped and nodded. Just as he started to speak, the man asked, "Would you like a job here this summer?"

Leo's eyes became bright. "Yes, sir. I sure would!" he said quickly. "I have a paper route in the afternoon. But in the morning I could water and feed the ponies. And I can be here every night." Then he added, "I can handle ponies well, sir. My dad has a pony called Paula. She pulls his flower cart."

"I hope you can work as fast as you can talk," the man laughed. "By the way, my name is Lorenzo."

"I can work fast, Mr. Lorenzo," he said. "And I can start right this minute."

In no time Leo knew the name of every pony. He watered and fed them and brushed them. Grumpy was first to be brushed.

"I guess no one has brushed you for a long time," Leo said to the pony. "You're full of mats and burrs."

Leo spoke kindly to the thin pony while he brushed out the mats and burrs. Grumpy tried hard to stand very still for Leo. But sometimes he nibbled on Leo's hair as if he were trying to talk to him.

After a while Mr. Lorenzo came by. "I've never seen that spotted pony stand still for anyone else," he said. "Either he likes you, or he's sick!"

Leo grinned at Mr. Lorenzo.

That afternoon, while Leo was walking his paper route, he thought about the bicycle he needed. Mr. Phillips had promised him a longer route as soon as he had a bicycle. Leo would have to save all his money. Maybe he could save enough to buy the bike at the end of summer.

After supper that evening Leo put on a clean shirt. He whistled all the way to the park. He liked making extra money.

Grumpy nickered when he saw Leo coming. Leo always stopped to pat Grumpy before starting his work.

But as the days went by, Grumpy seemed to be sick. One morning he wasn't on the path with the other ponies. Leo found him tied to a tree. He wouldn't eat a bite.

Leo thought about Grumpy as he watered and fed the other ponies. Then he went to see Mr. Lorenzo.

"Maybe Grump will feel better if I take him walking," Leo said. "There's grass over there by the duck pond. Maybe he'd feel better after eating some green grass."

"It's worth a try," said Mr. Lorenzo.

Leo untied Grumpy and led him to the duck pond. Grumpy panted as he walked.

At the pond Leo pulled some grass for the pony and whistled songs for him. Then, before long, it was time for Leo to go on his paper route.

"You're still panting, Grump," he said. "I won't take you back to the ride. I'll ask Mr. Lorenzo to watch you from where he is." He tied Grumpy to a tree.

That evening Leo brought Mr. Lorenzo to the duck pond. The pony lay very still.

"That pony isn't worth much any more. He's too sick for the children to ride," Mr. Lorenzo said. "I'll have to get rid of him."

Leo thought quickly. His dad kept Paula and the flower cart in their shed at night. Grumpy could stay there, too.

Leo gulped hard before he spoke. "Would you let me have Grumpy?" he asked.

"Why, you don't want a sick animal!" Mr. Lorenzo said. "I'm afraid that pony isn't going to be alive much longer."

"Maybe I could help him get well," Leo said. "Oh, please let me try!"

Mr. Lorenzo didn't say another word. He untied Grumpy. And together the three of them walked to the shed behind Leo's house. Grumpy was panting all the way. Almost out of breath, the pony lay down in one corner of the shed.

Mr. Lorenzo shook his head. "If he gets well, he's yours to keep," he said.

When Leo's mother found the sick pony in the shed, she guessed what had happened. Leo was always bringing home sick animals he had found. She carried a bucket of fresh water to Grumpy and gave him some medicine. Then she put some feed in Paula's bushel basket for Grumpy.

Later Leo's mother said, "You know we don't have enough money to feed another pony, Leo. If he gets well, he'll have to work for his keep just like Paula."

Leo promised his mother that Grumpy would earn his keep. "Don't worry," he told her. "I can buy food and medicine for Grump out of the bicycle money I saved."

During that summer Leo gave Grumpy his medicine and took him out in the sun each day. And each day Grumpy seemed to feel better. He ate as much from the bushel of feed as Paula ate.

One day, late in the summer, Leo decided to ride Grumpy down the street. The pony did not pant at all. Grumpy was well!

Leo was happy for his pony. But now what was he to do? He had already used most of his bicycle money to make Grumpy well.

"I'll ride my pony instead of a bike!" thought Leo. "Mr. Phillips may not say no to a longer paper route as long as I have something to ride!"

The next day Leo called Mr. Phillips on the telephone. "I'm ready for that longer paper route," Leo said. "I don't have a bicycle, but I have something just as good. Could you come by to see it?"

When Mr. Phillips came by that evening, he found Leo riding a spotted pony up and down the street. "See, I can ride Grumpy instead of a bicycle," Leo told him.

Mr. Phillips laughed. "If you can manage that pony, I'm sure you can manage a longer paper route," he said.

So the very next day Leo and Grumpy began their long paper route together.

THE WONDER OF IT

neigh   neighbor's   sleigh

flair   fairies   repairman

charge   bulge   agent   hedge

anybody   railroad   matchbox

rotate   excite   beetle

sewing

weight

hairpins

gadget

sandpaper

needle

scientist

inventor

company

vibrations

Why Don't You Invent It?

105

Inventors have filled the world with many kinds of inventions, but the need for more inventions never ends. You have probably heard other people say, "Why don't they think up a gadget that will—?" Maybe even you have said, "Why don't they—?" But you should have said, "Why don't I—?"

Why don't you think of a gadget before they do? You don't have to be a scientist to invent something.

One man who worked at a machine became an inventor. The machine shook him with such fierce vibrations that he lost weight. So every day he brought a rubber mat to stand on while he worked at the machine. When he stood on the mat, he didn't feel the vibrations so much.

But after work each day, someone took his rubber mat away. So the man cut out rubber and put it on the heels of his boots. This worked just as well as the mat. The man lost no more weight, and no one could take his boots away. Thanks to his idea, we now have shoes with rubber heels.

Another inventor, the son of a farmer, wasn't a scientist either. He thought of putting the eye of the needle in the point of the needle instead of putting the eye in the head. Everyone said it was all wrong. Silly! But it worked. And his idea led to the invention of the sewing machine.

Sometimes inventors get ideas from things they wonder about. One husband became an inventor after watching his wife pin up her hair. He wondered why she made a kink in the pins. His wife told him the pins with a kink would not fall out as the straight hairpins did.

This gave the husband who had wondered an idea. He started a company that made hairpins with a kink in them. Soon everyone bought the new hairpins.

You couldn't say the husband had really invented hairpins. He had just made them much better.

Another man got his idea from an empty matchbox. He saw that the sandpaper on one side of the empty box was as good as new. So he talked to the people at the matchbox company about putting sandpaper on only one side since the other half of the box was not used.

The matchbox company paid the man for his new idea. And the cost for its sandpaper was cut in half.

No, the need for inventions never ends. Why not ask yourself, "What ideas do I have that could become inventions?"

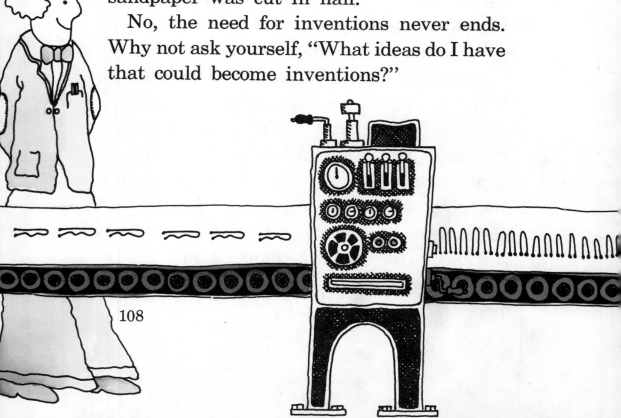

We work with words.

chipmunks chain torch

minds wildly binding

thud brothers gather breathing

solve budge prance

Sight word.

stomach

Sound the words.

cherry

grind

though

bulge

pieces

shoulder

Orville

customers

pretzel

trailer

studied

The Wonderful Machine

One day a big trailer full of junk rolled down the street and turned over right in front of Pete's house. There was the junk spilled all over the sidewalk. Pete thought it was wonderful.

The owner of the runaway trailer shook his head at the spilled junk, and then he just drove off. But Pete grinned. He sat down and studied the junk. Orville came and looked over Pete's shoulder.

"I have a book—" Orville began.

"I know," Pete said. "But first help me get this junk off the sidewalk!"

Orville and Pete carried the junk to the roof above Pete's apartment house.

"Now," said Orville, "I'll just go and get my book."

Pete and Orville studied the book. Then they studied the junk. After a while they looked at each other and nodded.

"We can do it," Orville said.

"Sure enough," said Pete. "And we might earn enough money to buy that small pup tent at Tinker's Store."

Pete and Orville started to work. First they made a sign for the front steps of the apartment.

Then the boys began to sort through the junk. There were springs and strings, a pan and a rusty bicycle spoke, pieces of old pipe, some small wheels, bottles, and steel balls, a few nuts and bolts, a dog leash, the lid of a trunk, and parts of an old steam engine.

The boys pushed and kicked and banged on the pieces of junk and set them together with the bolts. Then they put the parts of the steam engine together. Soon they had their Wonderful Machine ready.

"This Machine sure is creaky and wobbly," said Orville.

"Sure is pretty, though," said Pete.

Orville nodded. "We're ready. Let's get the gum stuff."

"And all the stuff for the jelly beans," said Pete.

"Gum is enough," warned Orville, who was always very careful. "The book says you never can tell about the Machine. It won't stand for too much."

"Oh, it'll be all right," Pete said. He was never afraid of anything. So the boys went to the store to buy the stuff.

Soon a group of children gathered on the steps of the apartment, waiting to see the invention. On the roof Orville was building a fire in the steam engine. Pete climbed to the top of the wobbly Machine and poured in the stuff for gum and jelly beans.

"All ready!" Pete called down to their customers on the steps.

The group rushed up the stairs and to the roof. A moment later the wheels of the old steam engine began to turn. The Wonderful Machine began to grind and shake. Balls were spinning, springs were thrashing, and wheels were turning. The Machine coughed and shook. Buzz, clump, creak! SCREECH, CLANG, ROAR!

Suddenly pink balls of bubble gum shot out of a pipe with a *ping, ping, ping*. The customers laughed and shouted. Soon Pete and Orville had sold all the gum balls for a nickel apiece.

Then out came jelly beans with a *floop, floop, floop*. Before long the boys had sold all of these, too.

Soon the Machine stopped and customers began to leave. Pete and Orville hurried to count their money. They had enough to buy the pup tent at Tinker's Store.

"If we make some pop," said Pete, "we'll have enough money for the bigger pup tent. Then we can both sleep outside."

Orville tapped Pete on the shoulder. "Gum and jelly beans are enough," he said. "The book says you never can tell—"

"Oh, it'll be all right," Pete said. "You keep the customers here while I go to the store." And he hurried off.

A little later cherry pop poured out from the Machine, too. And Pete and Orville had enough money for the bigger pup tent.

By late afternoon people from all over the neighborhood were coming to the roof. The Wonderful Machine shook, groaned, and roared. From its long pipe, customers got cookies, popcorn, cherry pop, cupcakes, and bubble gum.

But this still was not enough for Pete. "There aren't any pretzels," he said.

"You'd better watch out," Orville warned. "The Machine has an awful crack right in the middle of its smokestack. And it shot out some fire!"

"But if we make pretzels," said Pete, "we can buy the wall tent with that extra side room!"

Orville frowned. "The Machine is making some funny noises," he warned.

But Pete, who was not afraid of anything, rushed off to get the pretzel stuff.

Of course Orville was right. Pete never should have poured that pretzel stuff into the Machine. But he did. And when he did, wheels slipped and turned the wrong way, the power belt came untied, and the pan banged against the pipes. Bubble gum went *crack* instead of *ping*. Cherry pop splashed all over the roof. Cookies, popcorn, and cupcakes sailed into the air.

The Machine looked like a panting dragon. Its pipes coughed fire, and its smokestack sent huge rings of black smoke high above the apartment building. Then its lights flashed, its springs jingled, and a whistle blew. Nuts and bolts began to rain on the customers, and then—Ka-Phoom!

A huge cloud of black smoke rose high into the sky. The Wonderful Machine roared off the roof and sailed, spinning, into the air. Then it crashed back to the roof in thousands of pieces.

The customers stared at the pile of junk spilled on the roof.

Orville moaned and shook his head. "I told you not to do it," he said.

"Oh, well," said Pete. "We made enough money for the tent with the special cloth floor and the—"

Pete stopped. He and Orville stared at a big bulge of bubble gum growing from the pile of junk. The bulge grew bigger—and bigger—and bigger.

Pwack-zing! Something shot from the bulge and hit Pete in the stomach. "Ooo-oof!" he groaned. When it hit Pete in the stomach, it knocked him down.

Orville picked the thing up and took a sniff. Then he took a bite. He rolled his eyes from side to side as he swallowed the thing.

Orville grinned. "A pretzel!"

Funny the Way Different Cars Start

Funny the way
    Different cars start.
    Some with a chunk and a jerk,
    Some with a cough and a puff of smoke
    Out of the back,
    Some with only a little click—with hardly any noise.

Funny the way
    Different cars run.
    Some rattle and bang,
    Some whirrr,
    Some knock and knock.
    Some purr
    And hummmmm
    Smoothly on with hardly any noise.

by Dorothy W. Baruch

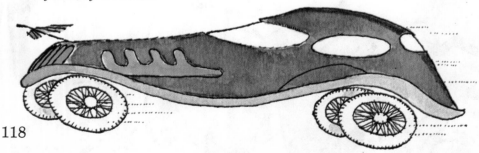

A Dream That Ran on Steam

Francis E. and Freelan O. Stanley were twins who lived many years ago. Between the two of them, many inventions were made. In time the brothers became famous.

One day the twins went to a fair. There they saw the first American steam carriage. Freelan O. nudged F. E. "That carriage sure sounds awful," he said. "All it does is cough and snort. And it can't even go two miles without stopping to build up some more steam."

"We could make a much better car than that one," said F. E., who was the bolder of the two.

"Indeed, we could," F. O. agreed.

Up to that time the brothers knew nothing about steam engines. But about one year later, their shop door opened. And out came the very first Stanley Steamer.

The brothers drove their steamer down the town streets. When they met horses, the horses took one frightened look at the smoking, steaming monster and then headed for open country. Soon everyone in the town was angry at the twins and their steamer.

So the brothers decided to make a steamer that didn't look like a monster. The Stanley twins read books about steam engines. Then they made an engine that was small enough to go inside a small car.

"A smaller engine? It's not possible!" everyone said. But the smaller engine was possible, and it worked very well. And the new car that the brothers invented didn't cough and snort like a monster.

One day the bolder F. E. said to F. O., "Let's play a joke on the town." Then he told F. O. his plan.

"Gee, cracky!" F. O. roared, slapping his knee. "We look just alike, and we'll dress just alike. People will sure think they're seeing double!"

In secret the twins built a second steam car just like the first one. Then their fun began!

F. E. drove down the street at 15 or 20 miles an hour. A policeman whistled for him to stop. While the excited policeman was yelling at F. E. for going far too fast, F. O. raced by in the other steamer. That poor policeman really thought that he was seeing double.

"Gee, cracky!" F. O. roared as he raced on down the street.

Some time later the Stanleys went to the first American car show to test their car against others in a speed race. The Stanley Steamer won!

In another race up a steep hill, not one of the other cars had enough power to climb it. But the Stanley Steamer climbed right to the top of that steep hill. Then almost everyone wanted a Stanley Steamer.

"Let's make cars to sell," said F. E.

"Indeed! Let's do," said F. O.

The burner in the early Stanley Steamers used kerosene for fire to make the water hot. When the water was boiling hot, it turned to steam. But sometimes the valves in the burner stuck, and the kerosene kept burning. When this happened, fire and black smoke shot out behind the car. It didn't hurt the passengers riding in the car. But the sight and smell of smoke frightened the people and animals along the road.

Firemen were often called to put out a fire in a Stanley Steamer. A fire engine pulled by horses rushed to the smoking car. The firemen used pumps to throw water over the hot steamer and its passengers. The engine would then speed away, leaving the passengers very wet and angry.

123

A Stanley Steamer could not be started quickly. There were water pumps, oil pumps, air pumps, and all kinds of valves to be opened. It took twelve or more minutes to get the little car started.

The twin brothers knew just how long it took for steam to build up in the engine. Just before the car was ready, F. O. would start walking down the street. F. E. would open the last valves and then run to catch up with F. O.

When the brothers were about a block away, they would turn and whistle, as if calling a dog to obey. By this time, the steam that had built up in the engine was enough to make the car start. Then the steamer would come straight down the street right to the Stanley brothers.

"Gee, cracky!" F. O. would shout, slapping his knee as he hopped in the car. "Our car comes to obey us like a fine dog!"

When a steamer came down the street, it did strange things to dogs. They became frisky and barked as they followed the car. At last the twins understood why.

Their engine made vibrations that gave out high-pitched sounds. People could not hear them, but dogs could. The high-pitched sounds and the sounds of a whistle were alike. So the dogs followed the sounds and barked.

When the Stanleys learned this secret, they decided to put a train whistle on each steamer to scare the dogs away. This same whistle gave the twins a trick to play on railroad men. The twins would drive to the railroad tracks and cross them, making no noise at all. Then they would blow the loud train whistle on the steamer and watch the railroad man rush out to the gate.

The railroad man would slam down a gate so no one could cross the tracks while the train was coming. Then the railroad man would wait—and wait—and wait for the train that never came.

The brothers would drive off merrily, and the railroad tracks became peaceful again.

No one knows what might have become of the Stanley Steamer if the twins had kept on working. One day the bolder Francis E. came steaming over a hill and saw a farmer with two wagons in the middle of the road. He didn't want to hit the farmer, so he ran off the road and was killed. And soon after that, Freelan O. stopped making the famous Stanley Steamer.

Today the Stanley Steamer is seen only in antique car shows. But some day steamers may be used again—steamers that run on atomic power. Gee, cracky! A possible dream on atomic steam?

balking taller chalky

native favorite imagine

wad Washington wasp

young swinging among hang

Mugli whole

squall

promise

washed

swung

rescue

closet

splinters

carpet

ferry

usually

possible

Go-Cart Magic

127

Some people just don't believe the real story of Bob's magic go-cart. But it wasn't a dream. I was there when it happened.

It began when my brother Bob got Dad and Mom to let us build a go-cart. Bob took the motor off an old power mower and put it on the go-cart. Putting in the motor sure took lots of work. But when we had finished, it ran swell.

I wasn't the one who told Bob he should paint it. That was Mr. Mugli, the old man who walked around our block each day.

Bob worked on the go-cart in the alley. And Mr. Mugli always came by to see how it was coming along. So Mr. Mugli was just as happy as we were on the day Bob drove it for the first time.

At first Bob rode the go-cart by himself, just to get the feel of it. After a while he took me for a ride. That motor from the power mower worked like a charm. I guess it was just about the best go-cart in this whole world.

"Now you should paint it," Mr. Mugli said to Bob.

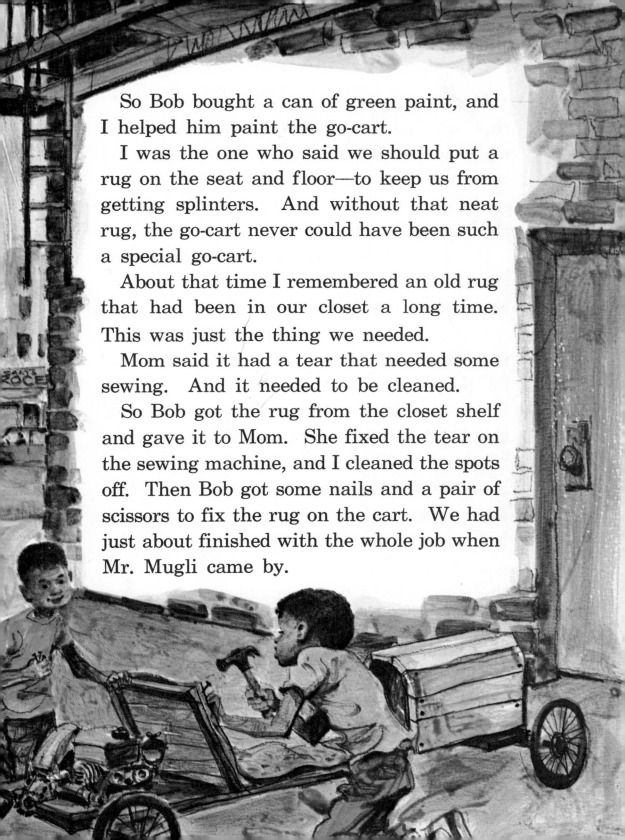

So Bob bought a can of green paint, and I helped him paint the go-cart.

I was the one who said we should put a rug on the seat and floor—to keep us from getting splinters. And without that neat rug, the go-cart never could have been such a special go-cart.

About that time I remembered an old rug that had been in our closet a long time. This was just the thing we needed.

Mom said it had a tear that needed some sewing. And it needed to be cleaned.

So Bob got the rug from the closet shelf and gave it to Mom. She fixed the tear on the sewing machine, and I cleaned the spots off. Then Bob got some nails and a pair of scissors to fix the rug on the cart. We had just about finished with the whole job when Mr. Mugli came by.

Mr. Mugli stopped as he usually did, but this time his head was cocked sort of funny as he looked at the rug. "Where did you boys get that rug?" he asked.

"In our closet," I told him. "Mom fixed the tear and I cleaned it."

Bob put another nail through the rug into the floor of the go-cart. Mr. Mugli shook each time Bob hit the nail.

"Stop!" he called to Bob. "I'll buy that rug from you. I'll give you five dollars for it."

Bob frowned. "Why didn't you tell me that before I put the nails in it?" he groaned. "The rug will tear if I try to pull it up now. And we need the rug so we won't get any splinters when we sit down. Besides, it looks pretty neat in the cart."

Bob took the pair of scissors to cut off the spare pieces we didn't need.

"No, no!" Mr. Mugli cried. "Don't dare cut it! It won't fly if you cut it!"

Bob stopped. "Won't fly!" he said. Then Bob got a funny look on his face. "You mean this is a magic carpet?"

Mr. Mugli nodded. "I guess I've said too much," he said. "This rug looks a lot like a magic carpet. But I can't tell for sure until I try it out."

"Go ahead!" Bob said.

Mr. Mugli said some strange words. The cart lifted off the ground and rose a few inches. Then a few more inches. When it was floating six or seven feet off the ground, Mr. Mugli said some more words. The cart sat down again.

"Wow! Look at that!" cried Bob.

"It's a magic carpet all right!" said Mr. Mugli. "And it has made your go-cart into a flying go-cart."

"Could I learn the words that will make it fly?" Bob asked.

Mr. Mugli thought about that. "Yes, I guess I could teach you enough to make it fly," he said. "But you'll have to promise to keep it secret."

"I promise," said Bob.

Mr. Mugli swung around to look at me.

"I promise, too," I said.

"All right," he said. "Be sure you are in the cart so it won't fly off all by itself. When you are ready, say, 'Over land, over sea, magic carpet, fly with me.' "

Just as Mr. Mugli said that, the go-cart rose again. Quickly he added, "Fly around, fly around, that's enough, put me down." And the go-cart floated down.

"Those are the words that bring it down," said Mr. Mugli. "Just remember, don't let anyone see you flying."

Well, Bob and I flew all over after that. We followed birds. We looked at roofs of tall buildings. It's possible that someone did see us flying around up there. But they probably thought we were a spaceship.

Then one day a brief squall came through and poured down rain. When it stopped, we heard on the television that the flood from the squall had washed out the main bridge at Pilot Springs. The people there couldn't get across the river. And there was no way to rescue them.

"Let's go out to the bridge and see if we can help," said Bob.

We drove the go-cart on a road so no one would see us flying. When we got to the bridge, some policemen and a rescue team were there trying to get a rope across the river where the bridge was out.

"Why do you want the rope across?" I said to the Chief.

"To help make a ferry," he said. "We will use the rope with an old ferry boat to tow the people over."

"I'll take the rope across," Bob said.

"In that?" said the Chief, looking at the go-cart. "Don't try to be funny!"

But Bob was feeling extra brave that day. He took the end of the rope and whispered the magic words.

The go-cart rose a few inches. Then it sailed right across the river a few inches above the water. Bob handed the rope to a man on the dock and came back. He hoped that the men were thinking he was floating instead of flying. But the Chief saw that the go-cart really flew.

"It's got to be magic!" cried the Chief. "No one has invented a gadget like that! I've never seen anything in the whole wide world like it!"

Well, the Chief already knew that it was some kind of magic. So Bob jumped out of the go-cart and showed the Chief our magic carpet. Then just to show how the spell worked, Bob said, "Over land, over sea, magic carpet, fly with me."

When the Chief and men on the rescue team saw the cart lift and float around, there was so much confusion that Bob forgot what he was doing.

"Hey, Bob!" I yelled.

Bob swung around. The go-cart was off the ground and headed west. "Wow!" he said, and then gulped a deep breath.

"The spell! Bring it back!" I cried.

Then Bob remembered. "Fly around, fly around, that's enough, put me down!" Bob said at last.

But the spell didn't work. The cart was too far away, and it kept right on flying by itself. Then it was gone.

The next day the story on the television was about the trouble from the squall in Pilot Springs. The man on television said a brave boy carried the rescue rope across the river on some boards. The man went on to say that the boards had later broken and washed away. But I know better, because I was there.

We hoped to see the go-cart again. But that was the last of Bob's invention. There will never be another go-cart like it, I know. I've talked to many an old rug since then. And none of them ever moved so much as three inches!

Think about This:

1 What other stories have you read in which special words made something magic happen?
2 Why do you think the man on television said that a boy had carried the rescue rope over the river on boards?
3 If you decided to make a go-cart, what would you use to build it?

wrinkle   wrench   written

guessing   guarded   guilt

quilts   questioned   queen

boss   blocks   tossed

edge   pigeons   budge

rake   shade   cone   decide

wringing

guiding

quite

Goff

hedge

mile

noticed

cucumbers

neighbor's

supposed

Sight word.

hour

Billy and the Power Mower

137

One hot day Billy went over to see if Fats could go swimming.

"I'm supposed to mow Mr. Goff's lawn," said Fats.

"That lawn? In hot weather?" said Billy. "You're crazy! It'll take a week."

"No, I'll finish in an hour easy," said Fats. "Mr. Goff has a new power mower— one of those big jobs."

"Oh, boy!" said Billy. "I'll come along and help you, Fats."

"I promised I wouldn't let anyone else touch it," Fats said. "You can come along and trim the hedge or rake the grass."

Billy didn't plan to rake or trim. But he still thought he might get to run the mower. So he went with Fats anyway.

Fats started the mower and roared off. Billy lay under a shade tree to watch. The new mower really was great! He wanted to run it more than ever. Besides, a cloud of gnats was swarming all around him. As he brushed the gnats away, he kept trying to think of a way to get his hands on that power mower.

"Hard work?" Billy shouted to Fats.

"Not at all!" Fats yelled back. "Guiding this thing is no trouble. It handles like a baby carriage."

After a few turns, Fats came over to sit in the shade. "Sure is hot," he said.

"I hadn't noticed, but I see your clothes are wringing wet," said Billy. "I'll run that mower for a while."

"I promised Mr. Goff no one else would touch his mower," Fats said.

"Okay! Okay!" said Billy. "But I hope you're not silly enough to be doing this just for fun."

"Well, it *is* fun," said Fats. "Plenty of kids would be glad to run a power mower. Besides, I make money at this job. I wish I could let you try it."

139

"Aw, those babies aren't so great," said Billy. "All that power, and you have to walk mile after mile just to mow the lawn anyway. It's too bad you can't do something about it."

"Like what?" asked Fats.

"Oh, fix it somehow so you can ride along while you're guiding it," Billy said.

"How could I do that?" asked Fats.

"Oh, I don't know," said Billy. "Right now I'm going for a swim. If I think of anything, I'll let you know."

Fats still had half the lawn to mow when Billy came back, pulling a wagon. In the wagon were his swim trunks, a towel, and about twenty-five feet of rope.

"What's the wagon for?" Fats asked as he stopped the mower.

"For you to ride in," answered Billy. He threw his towel and trunks on the grass and tied the wagon behind the mower.

"But if I stand up in the wagon, guiding the mower won't be easy. I'll have to stoop to reach the handles," Fats said as he studied Billy's rig.

"Watch," said Billy as he stepped into the wagon. "From the wagon, you can reach the handles and the motor, too."

Billy raced the motor. Then he pulled a lever. The mower darted ahead, and the wagon followed with a jerk. Billy grabbed the mower handles. He was headed straight for the garage.

"Stop it! Stop!" yelled Fats as he chased after him. "Push the lever down!"

Billy swung the mower around just in time to miss the garage. Then the mower, wagon, and Billy charged across the lawn.

"Push it down! Down!" Fats shouted.

Billy did something to a lever. But it didn't stop the wheels. Instead, it turned on the cutting blade.

The mower headed straight for Billy's towel and swim trunks. He missed the towel, but cloth from his swim trunks shot from under the mower in little pieces. By this time Billy's knees were knocking.

"Stop the cutting blade!" Fats called.

Billy was trying to reach the lever to the cutting blade when the mower suddenly slowed down. Then it gave a jerk and began mowing a path right on through the hedge! Then it took out full speed ahead, pulling Billy and the wagon after it. The next time it slowed down, there was a fresh smell of tomatoes and cucumbers in the air. Billy was mowing through the vegetables in the neighbor's garden! On he went, cutting off the tops of turnips and just missing a big watermelon.

Next the mower headed for the neighbor's house. Right at the back door it gave a snort, then coughed and died. As the motor died, Billy stepped out of the wagon quite terrified. His knees were so wobbly that he could hardly stand up.

Fats came running up, mad as hops. He wasn't worried about Billy, just about the mower that belonged to Mr. Goff. "You've done it now," he said.

The lady living there came out wringing her hands. She looked at the mower. Slowly she looked at her garden. Then she looked at Billy and Fats.

"We're sorry," said Billy. "The mower sort of got away from us."

"*Us?*" Fats shouted.

"I guess the tomatoes are finished," said Billy. "Your cucumbers don't look so bad, though. Salad is good with cucumbers and, uh, turnip tops. Could you maybe use them in a salad or something?"

Billy saw the scowl on the lady's face and decided she didn't think very much of his idea.

"If there's something I can do, I'll be glad for the chance," Billy said.

"Hmmm, I'll tell you what you can do," said the lady. "The boy who was supposed to mow my lawn can't do it. So you can just finish cutting what's left. Then you can trim along the hedge."

"Oh," said Billy, "well, I was just now going for a swim."

"What in?" asked Fats. "You'll have to rake your swim trunks off the lawn."

"But I don't happen to have a mower with me," Billy said, looking at Mr. Goff's.

"Not a chance!" said Fats. "When I finish Mr. Goff's lawn, I'm going to lock this mower in his garage."

"Oh, that's quite all right," said the lady. "You'll find an old push mower in my garage." Then she went into the house.

Fats pushed the power mower back through the hedge. "When I'm finished, I'm going swimming," he yelled at Billy. "Want me to wait for you?"

But Billy didn't answer. He just got the mower out of the lady's garage and then started pushing.

Think about This:

1 Why do you suppose Fats had promised Mr. Goff he would let no one else touch the mower?
2 What did Billy end up doing that he told Fats was a silly thing to do?
3 Why do you suppose Billy said, "The mower sort of got away from us," since he was the only one on the mower?
4 What did Billy say to the lady that he really did not mean?

Mr. Mudgett's Invention

Juan, Carlos, and Pedro stepped through the opening in the hedge between their backyard and Mr. Mudgett's.

"Are you sure he's gone?" asked Pedro.

"Yeah, I saw him leaving in his car a few minutes ago," answered Juan.

The three boys walked through the hedge and up to the strange red thing. For weeks they had watched Mr. Mudgett while he was building it.

"What is it?" whispered Pedro.

"How should I know?" said Juan.

"Maybe it's a spaceship," said Carlos.

"No, it can't be a spaceship. Its nose isn't cone shaped," said Pedro.

"I've got it now!" said Juan as though he had just discovered something. "It's a spy station. That porch up there is probably the lookout point."

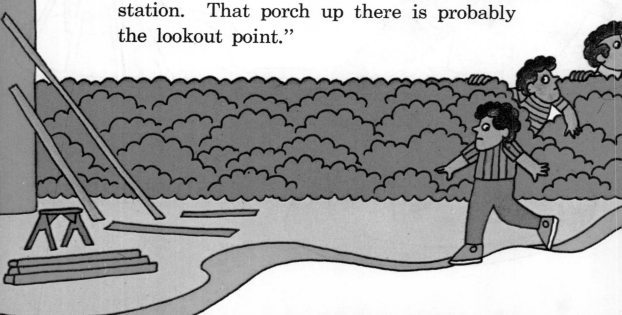

"Aw, why would he build a spy station in front of everyone?" asked Pedro.

"Probably so no one would suspect him," said Juan.

"Aw, why do you want to suspect Mr. Mudgett of being a spy?" said Pedro.

"Okay, don't listen to me," said Juan.

"Well, I want to know what that red thing is," said Carlos. "It's not cone shaped like a spaceship. And there is no reason to suspect Mr. Mudgett of being a spy. So let's just ask him what it is."

When Mr. Mudgett came back, that's just what the boys did.

Mr. Mudgett smiled at their question and said, "This is a new invention of mine, of course. I'm still working on it. I'll tell you what it is when it's finished."

"Well, then, I guess we'll just have to wait," said Pedro.

But as the three boys returned home, Juan shook his head at his brothers and asked, "You really didn't fall for that, did you? You don't think he's going to tell us what that invention really is!"

"Why wouldn't he?" asked Pedro.

"I tell you he's just fooling us," Juan replied. "He doesn't want anybody to know what that big red thing is."

"Juan, you'd suspect a harmless ant if you decided it looked funny!" exclaimed Carlos.

"Okay, you just wait and see. He's some kind of secret agent or something."

Every day after that, Juan, Carlos, and Pedro questioned Mr. Mudgett. "Is your big invention finished?" they would ask.

"No, not yet," Mr. Mudgett would say. "Maybe it will be tomorrow."

"Yeah, of course," Juan would always say to himself.

Then one day they saw Mr. Mudgett sitting on the steps of the red thing. He looked tired and upset.

"Well, is it ready?" asked Juan.

"I guess so," said Mr. Mudgett.

"What is it?" asked Carlos.

"I don't know," Mr. Mudgett sighed.

"Aw, come on now, why don't you know?" Juan questioned. This made him suspect Mr. Mudgett even more.

"Because every time I invent something, I find out it has already been invented," answered Mr. Mudgett. "So I wasn't going to tell anybody what this thing was, not even myself. That way I wouldn't invent something that was already invented."

"That was very clever," said Juan. But he didn't really believe Mr. Mudgett.

"Now I don't know what it is," sighed Mr. Mudgett. "I guess it's just a thing."

"Could we climb on the ladder up to the lookout point?" asked Carlos.

"Sure," said Mr. Mudgett, "if you think that's a lookout point. I hadn't thought of it that way."

Pedro and Carlos climbed right to the top of the red thing, but Juan didn't want to touch it.

"Would you like to go inside, Juan?" Mr. Mudgett asked.

Just as Juan was about to answer, his brothers called, "Hey, wait for us!"

"Well, climb down the ladder or slide down the slide," said Mr. Mudgett.

When Pedro and Carlos had slid down, Juan went inside with them. Mr. Mudgett bolted the door behind them. Why had he bolted the door? After that, Juan was extra careful of Mr. Mudgett.

Soon Pedro and Carlos discovered chairs that jiggled when they sat in them.

"Hold tight to the chairs and bounce," Mr. Mudgett said.

Juan wasn't about to join his brothers in this sport. He had already decided Mr. Mudgett was a secret agent, so it might be best just to watch and listen.

Pedro and Carlos jiggled and bounced so high in the chairs that they could almost touch the ceiling. The chairs looked like a lot of fun to Juan. But he still had not forgotten his idea about the bolted door and the clever Mr. Mudgett.

"What's the reason for the quilts on the walls and the ceiling?" Juan questioned.

"Just a minute, and I'll show you what those quilts are supposed to do," replied Mr. Mudgett.

He pushed a red button. The floor began to rock and tilt! This time there was nothing for Juan to do but join the others as the floor jiggled them.

Juan was trying to reach the bolted door. But the floor tilted to one side, and all the boys slid to the other wall. When they landed there, the floor tilted again. And the boys came sliding back where they had started from. Again and again the floor tilted, and with each tilt, the rocking got faster. Each time the boys bounced against the quilts, they tilted a little closer to the ceiling. Then they bounced right into it! Finally they were all laughing and thrashing into each other.

Mr. Mudgett pushed a black button, and the boys plopped together in the middle of the floor as it stopped.

"Wow, this is fun!" screeched Carlos.

"Yeah, it sure is!" exclaimed Juan.

"Do you want more?" asked Mr. Mudgett. "When I push the green button, the floor turns round and round."

This time the boys sat down and held onto each other. Mr. Mudgett pushed the button and the floor jiggled. Then it whirled. At first it whirled slowly, then faster and faster. Finally the boys whirled away from each other into the quilts.

When Mr. Mudgett pushed the black button to stop the floor, Juan was dizzy. He had forgotten all about that crazy spy idea.

"Now I can guess what that bolted door is for," Juan laughed. "It's to keep us from spinning into outer space! This is the best thing in the world!"

"Glad you like it," said Mr. Mudgett. "But now I have to give it away."

"Give it to us," begged Juan.

"What good will it be to you?" asked Mr. Mudgett. "I don't even know what it is."

"It'll be our very best toy," exclaimed Juan. "It can be our sliding, spinning, rocking—It can be almost anything! Our almost-anything toy!"

"Almost-anything toy!" Mr. Mudgett yelled. "Why, that's what I've invented!"

"May we have it? Please?" Carlos begged.

"Of course," said Mr. Mudgett. "You boys discovered what it is."

"Thanks! Oh, thank you!" the boys said.

"Thank you," said Mr. Mudgett. "Juan, you discovered a good name, all right. It is an almost-anything toy."

"It sure is," said Juan. He looked at his brothers and laughed. "It might even be used to send people into outer space!"

We work with words.

science scientist
wander swallow watery

Sight words.

mechanical million

Sound the words.

scientists
Washington
office
device
public
government
patent
receive

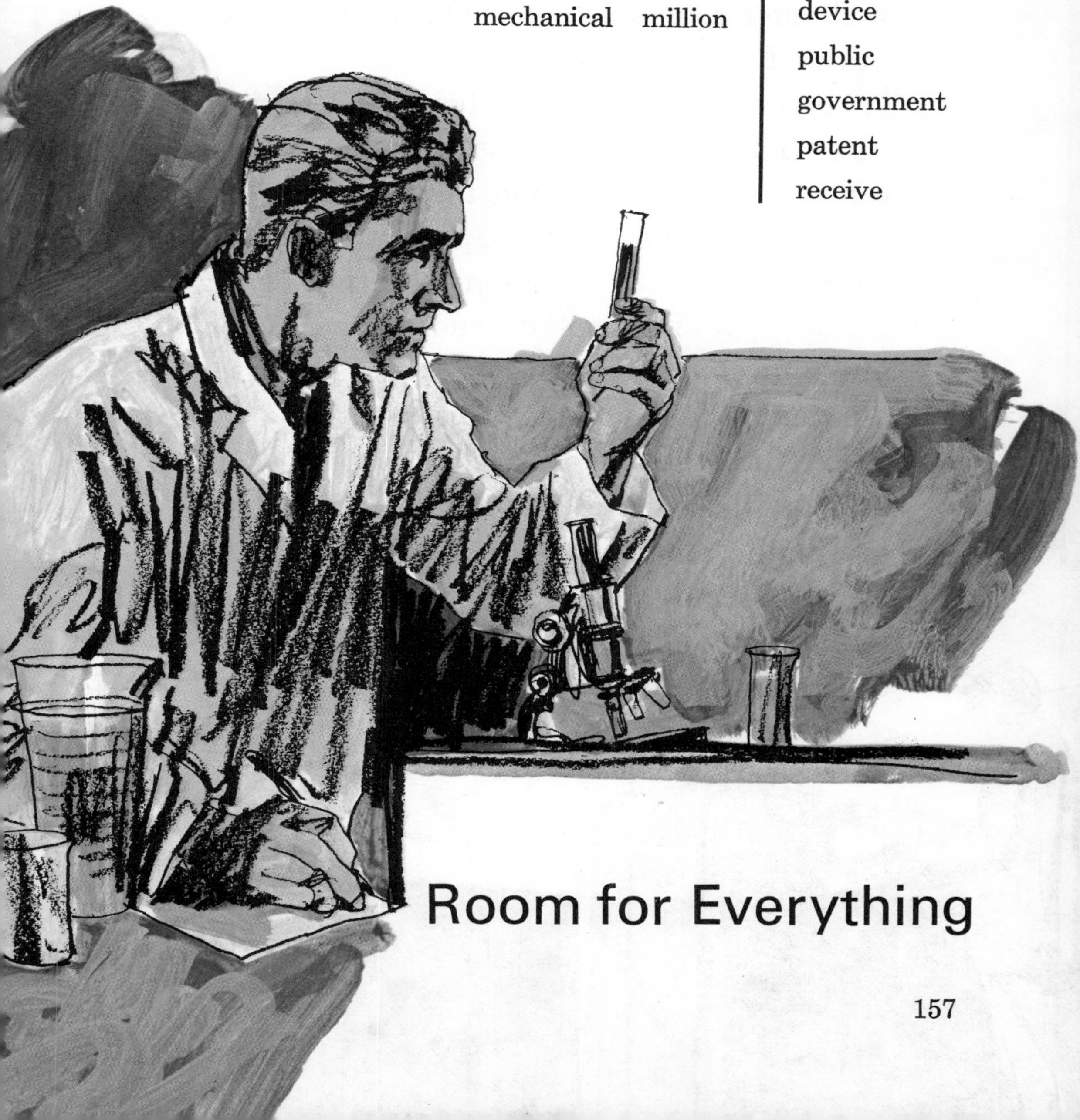

Room for Everything

In Washington, D.C., there is a room as long as a city block. Although there are drawings of more than three million things in this room, the United States Government will make room for more. This is the United States Patent Office.

The Patent Office is the home of American inventions. Almost everything that we use comes from an invention that someone has drawn and explained on paper and sent here. Drawings of such things as the first flying machine, a silent motor and a loud motor, and a mechanical device that makes nails— all can be found here.

The drawings of each invention are kept in the files of the Patent Office. There the public may visit to search through the files. Because eager scientists come here to find out what inventions have been made, the room is called the Search Room.

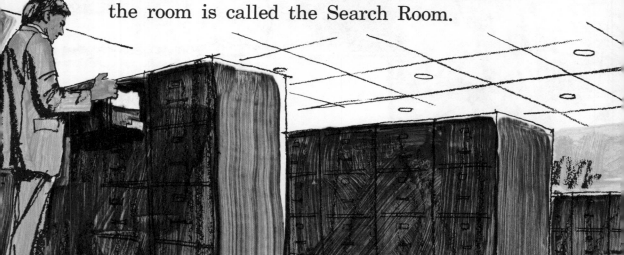

Many years ago it was difficult for an inventor to prove that he had invented something. Even if he had worked for years on an invention, someone might claim his idea. He could not prove that it was his.

But early in 1790 the Government of the United States passed a patent law to help inventors. Today, because of this law, an inventor can keep others from trying to claim his idea. All that he has to do is ask the Government to give him a patent on his invention.

Although patent laws are changed from time to time, scientists know the Patent Office is a safe place for their ideas. During the first seventeen years that the inventor has a patent, he has the right to let others use, make, or sell his invention. He has the right to ask others to pay him a fee if he lets them use it during this period. At the end of the seventeen years, he turns his invention over to the public. After this, the invention may be used by anyone who wants it. But no one may receive a second patent for it.

The first United States patent was given to someone who discovered a new way to make soap. This patent began the files on the more than three million different devices that have been given patents over the many years. If you searched the files, you would find that patents have been given for such things as the telephone, the television, and a device for making scrambled eggs.

An inventor doesn't have to get a patent for his invention. He may keep it a secret, or he may decide to give it to the world. If he has decided to keep it a secret, it may be because he thinks no one will copy his invention.

Someday if you invent something, you may decide to ask for a patent. If you do, you will first make a careful drawing of your invention. You will send it to the United States Patent Office in Washington, D.C. The people in the patent office will make sure that no one else holds a patent for the same invention. Then, if there is no other claim for your idea, they will send you a patent.

Along with an extra copy of your drawing, you will receive a paper that looks much like the one on this page. And a copy of your drawing will be put in the files with those three million drawings already in the Search Room.

But most important of all, the paper you receive will prove that your drawing is an invention. An invention that is all yours!

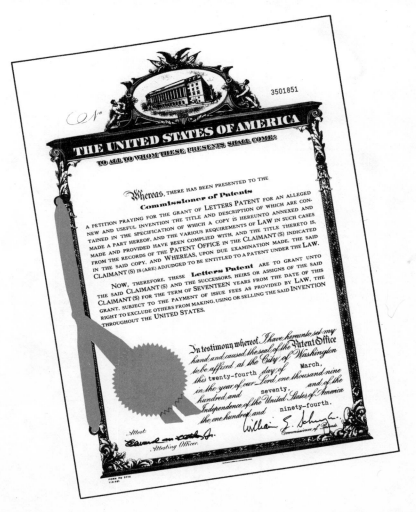

mountain ECHOES

We work with words.

tightly   flashlight   sighted

shallow   snowshoe   shapes

guarded   guilty   guest

fraidy-cat   thirty-nine   man-made

Sight word.

built

Sound the words.

fighters

swished

guitar

snow-capped

mountains

stilts

Danny and the Rangers

163

Alone in the Mountains

Danny Gray lived in a trailer with his dad. Danny's dad was an antique collector. Year after year they wandered about the country, stopping at places along the way to buy antiques and make a living.

Danny liked many things about his life. He loved the smell of a campfire and the sound of Dad's guitar in the evening. And he liked his dog, Nicky, who was always with him and kept him from being lonely.

But Danny still wished for a home with a yard and flowers. He wished to have some neighbors and a nearby school. This wish was secret, but it stayed with him wherever he went.

On one trip Danny and Dad drove up to the high country, where snow-capped mountains rose above a pine forest. They camped by a small cabin set high in the air on stilts. The cabin built on stilts was used as a lookout station by fire fighters. And some of them even slept there.

That night the fire fighters came over to the place where Danny and Dad were camped. They told tales while Dad played his guitar. Danny heard many tales of how great forest fires were started.

The next day Danny and Dad drove through the snow-capped mountains. But at the top of a steep hill, their car stopped.

"I was afraid this would happen," said Mr. Gray. "We're out of gas. There isn't another gas station until Cleo Springs, six miles ahead. Want to walk along?"

"No thanks, Dad. Nicky and I will stay here. I'll read my book while Nicky plays with the squirrels and chipmunks."

"All right, son. So long," Dad said. Then he started off for Cleo Springs, and Danny sat on the step of the trailer and read.

The chipmunks and squirrels chattered and scurried into places near Danny. Once Nicky barked at a chipmunk. It swished its bushy tail and scrambled up a nearby tree.

Then suddenly Danny closed his book and sniffed. "I smell something," he thought. He sniffed again. "It's a pine smell," he said as he looked up. There on a nearby hill was a puff of thick smoke.

"Come on, Nicky. Someone must have left a campfire burning," said Danny. He hurried down the road.

When Danny reached a turn in the road, he began to cough. The smoke was getting thick. He could see small flames.

"Hey!" Danny shouted. No one answered. Then Danny understood. Those small flames were the beginning of a forest fire. And he was alone in the mountains!

circle   mumbled   thistle

medal   interest   daddy

bridle   broken   amazing

marine   sardine   magazine

finger   dangling   twinkling

molding   boldly   scolding

halfway   hurray   haystack

thistles

reward

cedar

gasoline

blankets

smoldering

roadway

fainted

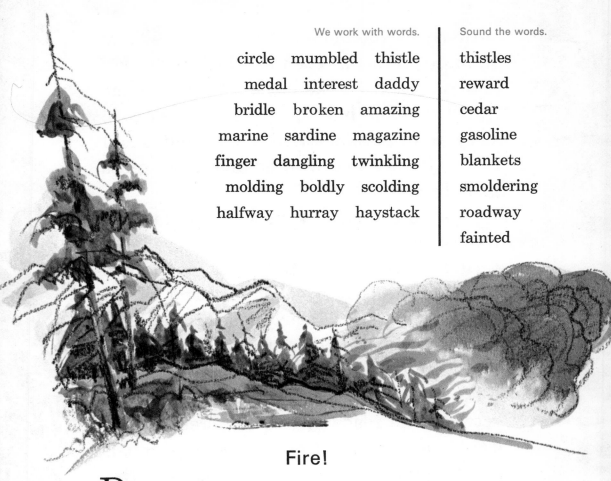

Fire!

Danny knew that the fire fighters would see the smoke from the lookout station. But he must try to keep the fire from spreading until the fire fighters got there.

He grabbed a bucket and two heavy Indian blankets out of the trailer. Then he ran down a slope to a nearby creek.

167

He threw the blankets into the creek and stamped on them. Then he filled the bucket and ran back up the slope. He threw the water on some burning thistles. S-s-s-s-sh! They were sizzling with steam, but small flames burned and whirled onto more grass and thistles.

"It's spreading! I must work faster!" Danny said to himself.

He hurried back to the creek for the two wet blankets. After wringing them out as best he could, he dragged them up the slope. He threw one over the burning thistles and the other over a blazing stump.

Danny knew that he must keep the fire between the roadway and the creek. This would keep the fire from spreading through all the pine and cedar trees until the fire fighters could get there.

"Come on, Nicky. We've got to keep the bucket filled," said Danny. "We've got to find every little fire and put it out." Nicky gave a sharp bark and followed Danny up and down the slope of the hill.

Sometimes Danny gave sharp commands to Nicky. "Dig! Dig 'em out!" With his paws, Nicky scattered the earth and stamped on it. This helped put out the smoldering grass. But as fast as one blazing fire was out, a new one took its place.

Danny was getting very tired. His back and arms hurt. One hand was burned. And his clothes were torn. He dragged the blankets up the slope once more and then fell to the ground near the smoldering fire.

"Won't someone help me?" Danny moaned to himself. "Can't the fire fighters see the smoke?" He was panting for breath.

Nicky was barking loudly. He had heard a high-pitched sound. As Danny looked up, he saw a helicopter coming down close to the roadway. But then he felt dizzy, and everything started swimming around in front of him.

Danny heard a voice say, "The fire is almost out." Then he fainted.

When Danny opened his eyes, his dad was holding him in his arms. "I'm so proud of you," said Dad. "But you've just fainted, so take it easy now."

From the helicopter a voice said loudly, "That's the boy!" And soon a tall forest ranger was standing beside Danny.

"Did you get the gasoline, Dad?" asked Danny, trying to smile.

"Never mind the gasoline," said Dad. "I want you to rest. The fire fighters will finish this fire."

"You did a very brave thing, young man," said the ranger. "If you hadn't guarded the cedar and pine trees on the other side of the roadway, they'd be burned to the ground. Thanks for taking care of them."

Danny smiled. He did feel proud.

"Now we had better fly you to town and have the doctor take a look at those burns and cuts," said the ranger. "You can meet us at the Ranger Office, Mr. Gray."

Danny felt better as he thought about riding above the earth in a helicopter.

When they landed in town, a doctor put medicine on Danny's burns, and the ranger bought him some ice cream. Then they went back to the Ranger Office. Danny found his dad talking to the head ranger.

The ranger looked at Danny. "There's the bravest young man in all the forest," he said. "Your dad and I were just talking about what you might like for a reward. What kind of reward would you like?"

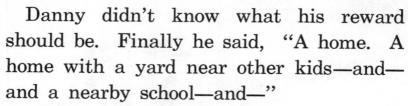

Danny didn't know what his reward should be. Finally he said, "A home. A home with a yard near other kids—and—and a nearby school—and—"

The head ranger and Dad looked at each other and laughed.

"There's a log cabin down by the lake," said the ranger. "It's not built on stilts, but it's got a yard and a nearby school. You can move in tomorrow since your dad has decided to take a job with me."

The next morning Danny and his dad and Nicky walked down to the log cabin. Pine and cedar trees guarded it on all sides. Inside, Danny found a large living room, a warm fireplace, and carpet on the floor. Nicky lay down on a rug in front of the fireplace as though he were there to stay. And Danny wondered if Nicky hadn't once had a secret wish, too.

pear   nearly   searches   beard

furnace   bandage   senate

America   aboard   among   alert

shallow   blizzard   supplies   gallons

troll   post   folks

eighty   neighbor   weigh

whiz   whine   whether

reins

fear

passage

alarmed

bottom

colt

neighed

whisper

lying

helpless

listened

shivered

Ghost Horses

A hard knock on her door woke Kim in the middle of the night. Her mother called in an alarmed voice, "Wake up, Kim! Dusty is out of the barn and has run off again. You must help us find her before the storm gets here."

"Oh, no!" moaned Kim. It was so peaceful lying in her warm bed.

"We have to do things like this if we're to run a ranch, Kim," her mother explained. "Hurry, dear. Daddy and Slim are saddling horses for us."

Mother's voice faded away as she walked downstairs. Kim wanted to be left alone. She shivered under the sheet at the thought of the damp, stormy night.

Mother called again, "Hurry, Kim!"

Kim put on her riding clothes and ran to the barn. Slim was saddling Cricket for her. "You stay away from Giant's Backbone, Kim," he said. "On a black stormy night like this, ghost horses travel through the passage over those hills."

"Ghost horses!" cried Kim, alarmed. "Oh, Slim, have you ever seen them?"

"No, but I've heard them on stormy nights in that passage over the hills," said Slim. "I could hear those horses' hoofs beating each time bolts of lightning struck and thunder roared."

"What did you do?" asked Kim.

"I was so shaky I hid behind a tree for a while. Then I ran home," said Slim. His voice faded to a whisper as he added, "This happened a long time ago, but I still won't go along that passage in a storm."

Slim had finished saddling the horses, and he handed Cricket's reins to Kim. She gripped the reins and shivered.

Dad came up and handed Kim a flashlight. "We'll all look in different places, Kim. You take the higher field."

Kim shivered. The higher field was close to Giant's Backbone. Mother gave her a sharp look and said, "Everyone has to do his part to find Dusty."

Kim rubbed Cricket's nose. "Are you as scared as I am, boy?" she said.

Cricket neighed softly and stamped on the floor of the barn.

Kim held the reins and got on Cricket's back. Just then a gust of wind blew the barn door open. The air smelled damp, so the storm must be near.

When Kim reached the higher field, she found the gate open. "Giant's Backbone! Of course, that's where Dusty would go," she said to Cricket in a whisper. "Will we have to go in there alone?"

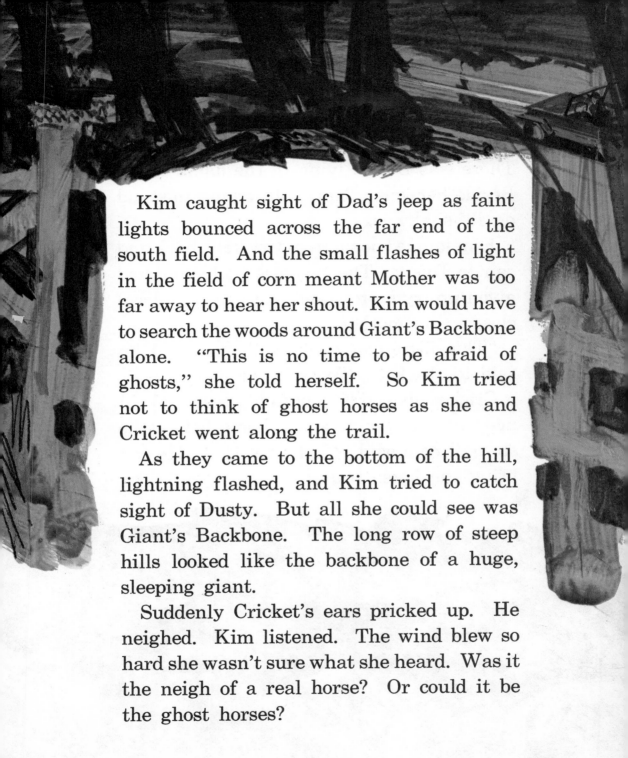

Kim caught sight of Dad's jeep as faint lights bounced across the far end of the south field. And the small flashes of light in the field of corn meant Mother was too far away to hear her shout. Kim would have to search the woods around Giant's Backbone alone. "This is no time to be afraid of ghosts," she told herself. So Kim tried not to think of ghost horses as she and Cricket went along the trail.

As they came to the bottom of the hill, lightning flashed, and Kim tried to catch sight of Dusty. But all she could see was Giant's Backbone. The long row of steep hills looked like the backbone of a huge, sleeping giant.

Suddenly Cricket's ears pricked up. He neighed. Kim listened. The wind blew so hard she wasn't sure what she heard. Was it the neigh of a real horse? Or could it be the ghost horses?

177

Cricket trotted on as Kim let him set the pace. Then suddenly he stopped with a loud neigh. Kim turned on her flashlight. There was Dusty, lying in the damp grass. Beside her was a baby colt, trying to stand on its shaky legs.

Kim jumped down from Cricket's back and ran to Dusty. The helpless little colt had given up trying to stand and had lain down close to its mother.

"This little colt can't walk home," Kim said to Cricket. "What'll we do?"

Cricket nudged Kim with his nose. "We'll need help to get this colt home before the storm," Kim said. "Let's get Dad. He can bring the horse trailer."

But it was a long way back around the hill, and Kim must hurry. "Going across Giant's Backbone sure would save time," Kim thought. Then she listened to the wind and thought of the ghost horses.

"I'm just too scared to take the short trail over that hill!" she said. "I'll have to think of another way."

The wind whistled. Lightning flashed. That did it! The sight of the lightning made Kim change her mind. The colt was so helpless! Scared or not, Kim had to take the short passage over the hills. There was no other way.

"Get along, Cricket. We have to go across Giant's Backbone," Kim said as she jumped onto the horse's back. Cricket started up the hill.

As they climbed higher, the rocks made strange shapes that looked scary to Kim. Her hands gripped the reins. All at once she heard a new sound. She heard hoofs and the neigh of a horse. It was—it must be the ghost horses! Shaking with fear, she laid her head down on Cricket's neck.

The wind stopped, and Kim listened. Now she didn't hear the beating hoofs.

"Why didn't Cricket neigh in answer to the horses?" thought Kim.

Again the wind whistled around the rocks, and Kim heard the beating hoofs. She looked at Cricket's ears. They weren't pricked up, and he didn't seem to be alarmed. Hadn't he heard them?

Now they were on top of Giant's Backbone, and again she heard the hoofs of the ghost horses. Where were they? Kim shivered in fear. But Cricket just walked along.

Again the wind died away, and the sound of the ghost horses faded. All at once a thought came to Kim, "Was that sound really coming from horses, or—?"

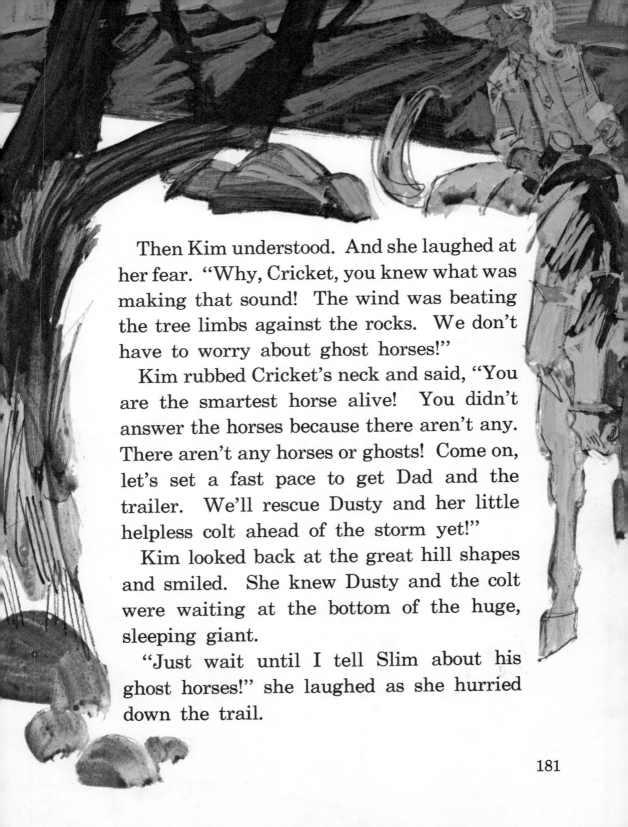

Then Kim understood. And she laughed at her fear. "Why, Cricket, you knew what was making that sound! The wind was beating the tree limbs against the rocks. We don't have to worry about ghost horses!"

Kim rubbed Cricket's neck and said, "You are the smartest horse alive! You didn't answer the horses because there aren't any. There aren't any horses or ghosts! Come on, let's set a fast pace to get Dad and the trailer. We'll rescue Dusty and her little helpless colt ahead of the storm yet!"

Kim looked back at the great hill shapes and smiled. She knew Dusty and the colt were waiting at the bottom of the huge, sleeping giant.

"Just wait until I tell Slim about his ghost horses!" she laughed as she hurried down the trail.

Cloud Horses

Sitting on a hilltop
  Beneath a windy sky
And all about me the summer's hum:
Nothing like it, on earth or on high—
The cloud horses, cloud horses, cloud
    horses come!

Storming down the twilight,
  Straining at the dawn,
With streaming manes they carry on:
Silently galloping, vanishing some—
The cloud horses, cloud horses, cloud
    horses come!

by John Travers Moore

182

We work with words.

gallons medal heaven levels
whey hockey prey Smokey
auction sawed paused taught
dangled itself farther
somebody underground snowdrift

Sound the words.

currents
valley
haul
canyon
mountainside
supplies
flume
logger
lumber
lumbermen
trough
shallow
mountain

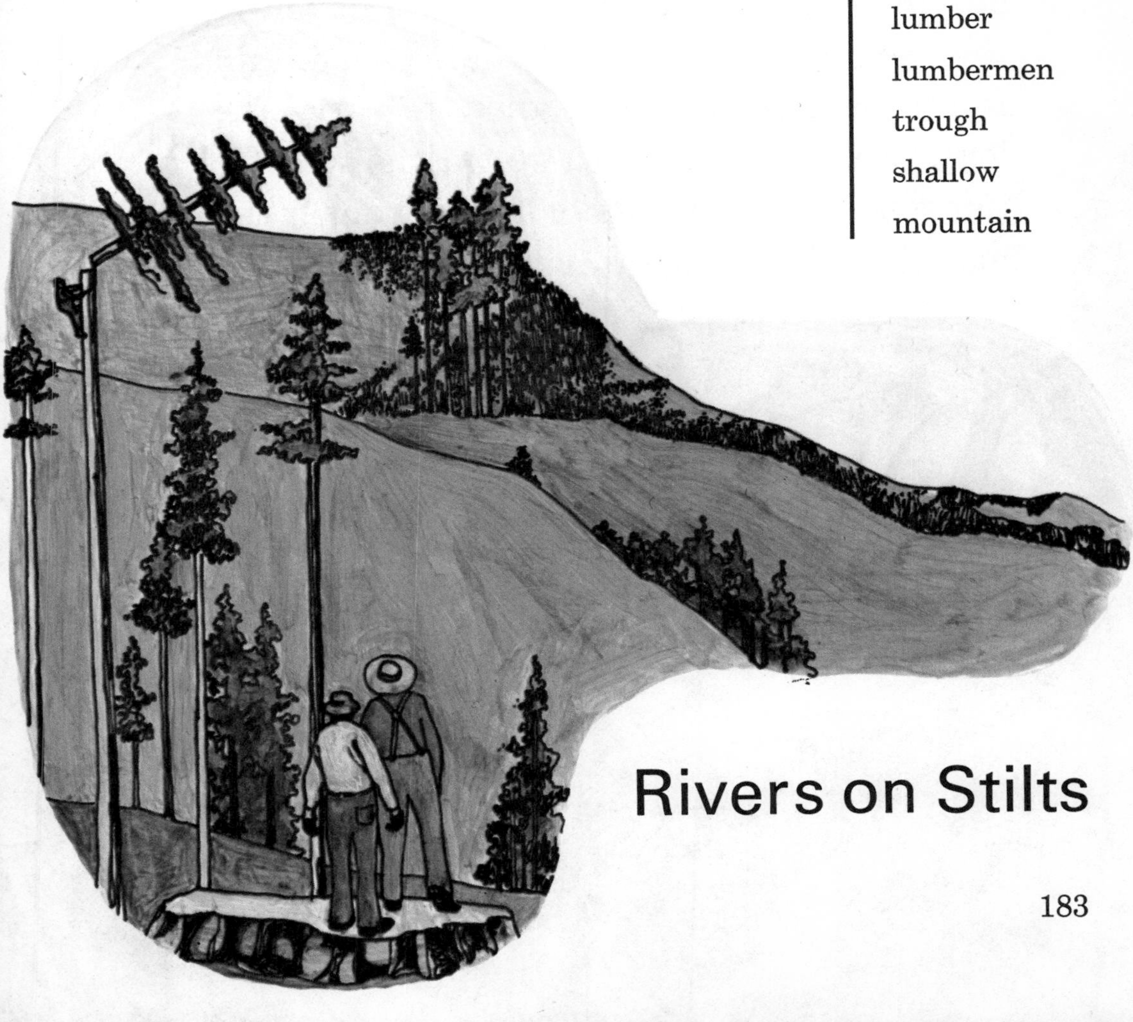

Rivers on Stilts

Everyone knows that our great rivers are used by boats to carry heavy supplies. But mountain rivers are so swift they can upset and break up any boats but the smallest of canoes. So mountain rivers are not often used to carry heavy supplies.

In the mountains near these swift rivers great trees often grow. But the mountain slopes are steep and rocky. Trucks can't get in to haul the cut logs or lumber to the lumber mills. And the swift mountain rivers nearby are too shallow to carry the logs. So at one time there was no way for lumbermen to get logs or lumber down the mountainside to a railroad or truck.

But lumbermen have learned how to take care of this problem. They have learned how to build man-made rivers. They use water from mountain rivers to build their own rivers to carry the logs or lumber down the mountainside.

The man-made river is a shallow wooden trough built in the shape of a V. It may be about a foot and a half wide at the bottom and four or five feet wide at the top. When a mountain stream is fed into this trough, the water runs through it about two feet deep. This wooden trough is called a *flume,* and the water that runs down it makes it truly a man-made river.

The flume itself has to be built over one deep valley and canyon after another on its way to the bottom. The lumbermen build the flume on wooden stilts, much like those found under a railroad bridge.

At places along the main flume, shorter flumes sometimes carry logs from different spots in the mountains. These logs float down the shorter flumes until they join other logs in the main flume itself. Then they are carried across each canyon and valley to the bottom of the mountain. There at a mill the logs are cut into boards. A railroad train or a logging truck waits to take the cut logs or boards farther on their trip.

But sometimes the logs do not ride easily down the flume. Sometimes logs get stuck in the flume and make a logjam. One log gets stuck in the flume, and others pile up behind it. The logjam stops the water like rocks in a dam.

The water behind the logjam gets deeper. As it gets deeper, the logs float higher and higher in the flume. This is why the V shape of the flume is so important. As the logs float higher in the flume, they have more room near the top of the V, so they can often break free. Then the logs can float down the flume once again.

But a logjam cannot always free itself. So a logger works at key places along the flume to keep it open. Sometimes at night the logger hangs a bell in the flume of logs. As long as the bell rings, the logger knows that the logs are clapping against it as they go down the trough. But if the noise stops, he knows there is a logjam.

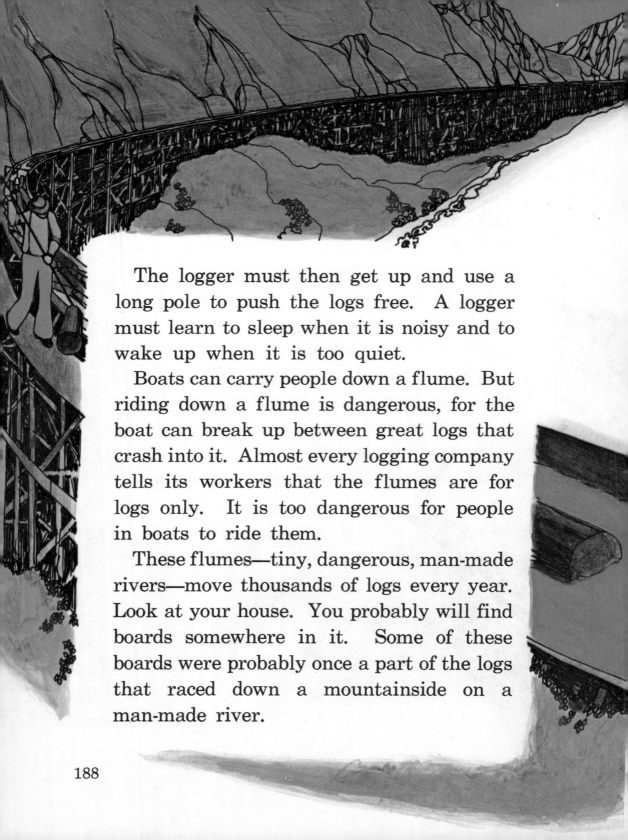

The logger must then get up and use a long pole to push the logs free. A logger must learn to sleep when it is noisy and to wake up when it is too quiet.

Boats can carry people down a flume. But riding down a flume is dangerous, for the boat can break up between great logs that crash into it. Almost every logging company tells its workers that the flumes are for logs only. It is too dangerous for people in boats to ride them.

These flumes—tiny, dangerous, man-made rivers—move thousands of logs every year. Look at your house. You probably will find boards somewhere in it. Some of these boards were probably once a part of the logs that raced down a mountainside on a man-made river.

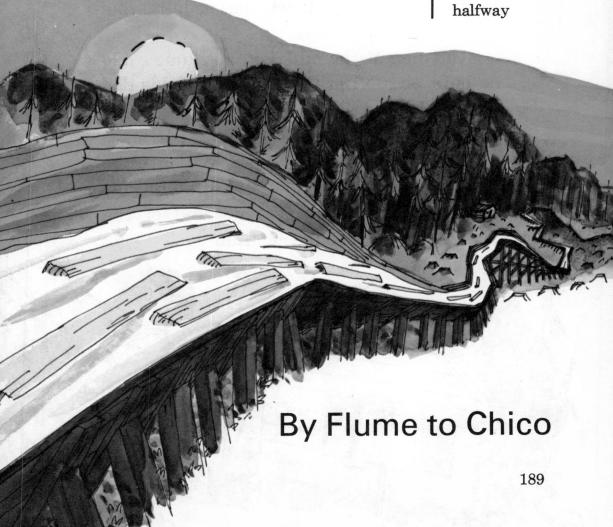

By Flume to Chico

189

Barney lived in a logging camp high in the Sierra Mountains. In the mill near his cabin, great logs were cut into boards of rough lumber. Then the lumber was sent to the mills in Chico, thirty-nine miles down the valley.

As soon as the sun rose, Barney's father dressed in heavy logging clothes and boots. While he ate breakfast, he usually told tales about the flume.

"The men at the mill said no flume could be built across Big Chico Canyon!" his dad said. "But we showed 'em! Now it takes only two hours by flume to Chico. It takes eight hours to travel by road. We have the best flume in the Sierra Mountains!" Barney and his mother never grew tired of the tales Dad told about the flume.

Barney wanted more than anything to ride a flumeboat someday. It was dangerous. One man had been killed that way. But Barney still wanted to ride the flume.

"Sure, flumeboats are dangerous!" his dad said. "But when time is truly important, it sure beats going around by the road. That's why I built an extra strong boat."

One morning Barney watched Dad leaving for work, his bright ax swinging at the end of his arm. Then Barney decided to go cut some logs, too.

Six weeks ago it had taken Barney forty strokes to cut through a log. But he had practiced swinging the ax and breathing just so. The day before yesterday he had cut a log in ten strokes. And yesterday he had used just eight strokes.

"Today I'll do it in six!" Barney said.

Barney chose a log that seemed to be the right size. He raised the ax, gripped the handle tightly, and braced his knees.

Whap! Whap! Splinters of wood shot out. Whap! He had cut more than halfway into the log.

"If only Dad could see me now!" Barney thought.

His final strokes must be clean in order to finish the log. Barney braced the log with his foot. Then he raised the ax.

The ax was halfway down when Barney's foot slipped. Suddenly a sharp pain shot up his leg. He stared at the blood collecting outside his shoe.

"Mother! Mother!" he called as he hopped toward the cabin.

"Oh, Barney!" his mother cried. "I've been afraid this would happen!"

Quickly she made Barney lie down on the ground. "Easy, Barney," she said softly. "I'll be right back."

Soon his mother returned with water and a clean towel. She washed his foot. Then she used a towel as a bandage. She bound the cut tightly to stop the blood.

"Now, Barney," she said. "We've got to make it up to the doctor's cabin. Brace yourself against me and hop."

"B-but, Mother!" Barney cried. "Don't you remember? This is the doctor's week to be down in Chico!"

"Well, then, this is it!" said Mother, her face set tightly. She bundled Barney in his coat and brought one for herself.

"Are we going after Dad?" asked Barney.

"There isn't time," Mother said. "Your father is cutting logs on the other side of the mountain."

"Then where can we go?" Barney asked.

"You'll know soon enough," Mother said.

Barney braced himself against his mother and hopped along. When they came near the flume, Mother stopped him.

"Here we are, Barney," she said.

Barney's heart raced. They were standing by Dad's flumeboat.

"Get ready, Barney!" Mother called. "All right. Now!"

The boat hit the water. Quickly Mother stepped aboard and helped Barney aboard with his bundled foot. Then suddenly they shot down the flume toward Chico.

In the flumeboat Barney felt as though he were flying on a cloud. The pine forest rushed by as they raced toward the valley.

194

Far, far below was Big Chico Creek at the bottom of the canyon. Even with the pain in his foot, Barney was excited. He was truly riding the flume, bound for Chico!

All at once the flumeboat swung round a curve. With a thud, the boat jammed between great boards of lumber. The racing water lifted the flumeboat and the boards higher and higher in the trough. Then, just as suddenly, the jam broke. The boat leaped on down the flume toward the valley.

Into the forest they darted, halfway to Chico. Then Barney saw a logger. He was braced against a long pole, watching the lumber go by. The logger was surprised when he saw the boat. But when he saw blood and the bandage on Barney's foot, he shouted and waved them on.

Down the shallow currents of the river they sailed, the loose boards of lumber floating with them. They were less than an hour from Chico.

Then suddenly they flew round another curve. Just ahead, the flume was jammed.

"Mother! Mother!" Barney cried.

"Brace yourself, Barney!" Mother called.

They hit the jam with a terrible thud. Lumber coming from behind crashed into the back of the boat. The boat did not break. Barney's father had built it well. But now Barney and his mother were raised higher and higher behind the jammed boards.

"We're going to wash over the edge into the canyon!" Barney cried.

Feeling dizzy and sick to his stomach, Barney almost fainted as he looked down at the canyon far, far below. His heartbeats echoed loudly in his ears.

"Iron Canyon!" called Barney's mother above the roar of the river. Her fingers gripped Barney's shoulder. "Don't give up, Barney! Don't move! Just hang on and stay aboard!"

Barney shivered. He held on so tightly that it seemed as though his breathing had stopped. Then he heard a loud crack as the jam broke. The boat slowly pushed away from the edge of the flume.

Once more they were moving down with the river of lumber. Just ahead lay Chico and the doctor. Barney's heartbeats began to set a steady pace. They had made it safely. The ride down the flume was over.

Think about This:

1 What could Barney's mother have done to stop the blood instead of putting a bandage on the cut?
2 Why did Barney and his mother use the flumeboat, since riding the flume was so dangerous?
3 How do you think Barney and his mother got home, since they could not ride back up the flume?

198

soul   plow   thousand   hollow

remove   snowshoe   movers

craziest   poem   funnier

perhaps   mumbled   athlete

nobody   begins   nation

blizzard   pellets   fluffy

gnome   knight   gnawing   knob

snowdrift

lose

carrier

Carson

America

struggled

known

article

Olympics

numb

California   John   Thompson

honor   skis

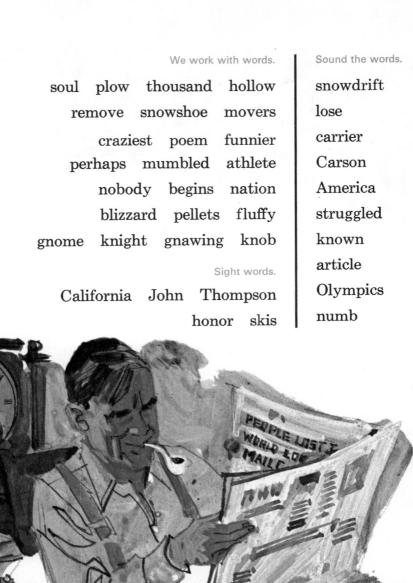

Snowshoe Thompson

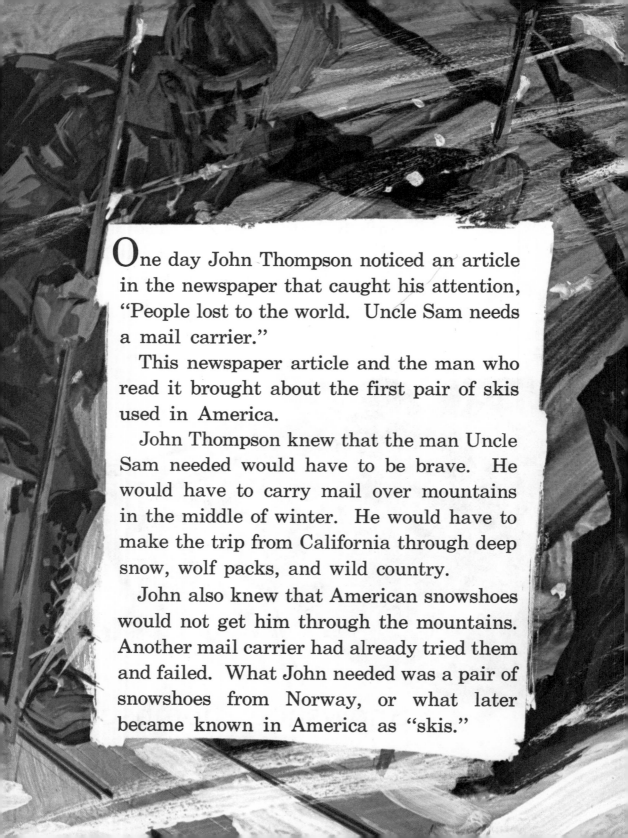

One day John Thompson noticed an article in the newspaper that caught his attention, "People lost to the world. Uncle Sam needs a mail carrier."

This newspaper article and the man who read it brought about the first pair of skis used in America.

John Thompson knew that the man Uncle Sam needed would have to be brave. He would have to carry mail over mountains in the middle of winter. He would have to make the trip from California through deep snow, wolf packs, and wild country.

John also knew that American snowshoes would not get him through the mountains. Another mail carrier had already tried them and failed. What John needed was a pair of snowshoes from Norway, or what later became known in America as "skis."

John had come to America from Norway. He still remembered how the people in his country made snowshoes. So he sawed and shaped some green wood and made a pair.

Then John set out to cross the mountains with a 100-pound sack of mail and supplies strapped to his back. No one thought he could make it. But John had to try.

On his third day out, John ran into real trouble. Large fluffy snowflakes had been coming down half the morning. Then they changed to frozen pellets of ice. And John knew he was in for a blizzard.

He began to think he would never reach Carson Valley. The wind whistled through the mountains and bit into his face. The frozen pellets of ice hit him harder and harder with each cold blast of wind.

He struggled slowly ahead, the 100-pound sack of mail still strapped to his back. He had to make it to Carson Valley and the people who were cut off from the world.

But the blizzard did not let up. Time and time again John almost turned back. But each time he told himself, "I must not be alarmed or lose hope. The storm just has to let up soon."

So he struggled slowly ahead. His arms were so tired they were numb. Finally the pellets of ice seemed to lose some of their bite. John thought maybe his face was so numb that he could no longer feel them. But after a while, the wind lost its whistle, and the pellets of ice turned into fluffy snowflakes again. The blizzard was over. And not far away, John could see the roof of a cabin.

John knocked at the cabin door and heard a small voice say, "Thank God! Come in!"

Inside, John found a man lying on the floor, too sick to get to his bed. Both of his feet were frozen numb, and the man was almost dead from the cold.

John gathered some wood and built a fire. To feed the man, he made water from snow and used it to make soup from the dried beef in his mail sack. This man needed a doctor. So John stepped outside to see if he could get through to the valley.

The snow had stopped. There, far below, he saw a puff of smoke climbing into the sky from what looked like a huge snowdrift. Carson Valley! He had made it!

He strapped on his skis. "Whoopee!" he shouted as he started down the slope.

"Whoopee!" must have been heard by the people in the valley. For in a few minutes, John could see them as they struggled to meet him at the top of the snowdrift. And when they discovered that the mail had come through, the people cheered. John Thompson, the mail carrier, had not failed. And the forgotten people were a part of the world again!

That night John sawed and shaped skis for a rescue party. Then he went with the rescue party to bring the sick man to a Carson Valley doctor.

Soon John Thompson became famous. He was known as "Snowshoe Thompson." He showed the people in the mountains of the West how to make and use skis. Most of the people made their own. In a short time, most of them were skiing well.

So, when the Winter Olympics were held some time ago in California, it was as if the world had come to honor the man who brought skiing to America. To honor the people of the West and to honor Snowshoe Thompson.

We work with words.

contraption auction nation
bamboo nook cooling
wormy worthless worse
cord nor thorny
expert excuse example explore
cruel violin merriest
Snakey spinney Smokey

Sight word.

women

Sound the words.

nations
swoop
world's
torch
exciting
skier
hockey
pigeons
athlete
practice
bobsledding

Winter Olympics

Every four years young men and women of the world's nations gather at the Winter Olympics. In the snow and ice of mountain country, they gather for games of skiing, skating, bobsledding, and hockey. The best young men and women in each game win an Olympic Gold Medal.

To win a gold medal in the Olympics is the most exciting honor that can come to an athlete. For years each athlete has been getting ready for this event. Each has had to work hard and practice long hours. Each has long hoped to win a gold medal.

Now, at last, his moment has come.

High in the mountains people are gathered. Flags of many nations wave in the cold air while a band plays lively music. One by one the athletes march into the snow and stand, each behind the flag of his nation.

Suddenly a skier swoops down a nearby mountainside, carrying the Olympic Torch. He is cheered by the crowd as he lights the Olympic Flame, which stands for peace among the world's nations. When the flame is lit, voices sing the beautiful Olympic Song.

In the silent snow, one athlete steps out
in front of the crowd to say the Olympic
Oath. He says the oath for himself and all
the athletes. Then several hundred pigeons
swoop into the bright, cold sunshine. The
pigeons are set free in honor of peace.

As the time comes for the games to begin,
the athletes become more and more excited.
Their thoughts turn to one thing only—the
games that are to come. They wish that they
could get away from the crowd and judges to
practice one more time. Then the Olympic
games begin. And one of these games is the
ski-jumping event.

With great speed, a skier trails down a slide, raised high above the ground. As he leaves the end of the slide, he is shot high into the air, his body pointed over his skis. He must try to jump farther than any other skier. He must hold his strong body very steady for a fine landing at the bottom of the jump. Any lively gust of wind could send him crashing down with the speed of a man falling from a tall building. How exciting and dangerous!

Yes, dangerous it is. But danger doesn't scare the athletes. No event at the Winter Olympics seems too dangerous for them. They keep trying to win a gold medal in games of hockey, ski-jumping, bobsledding, skating, and other events. The gold medal means they are the world's best athletes.

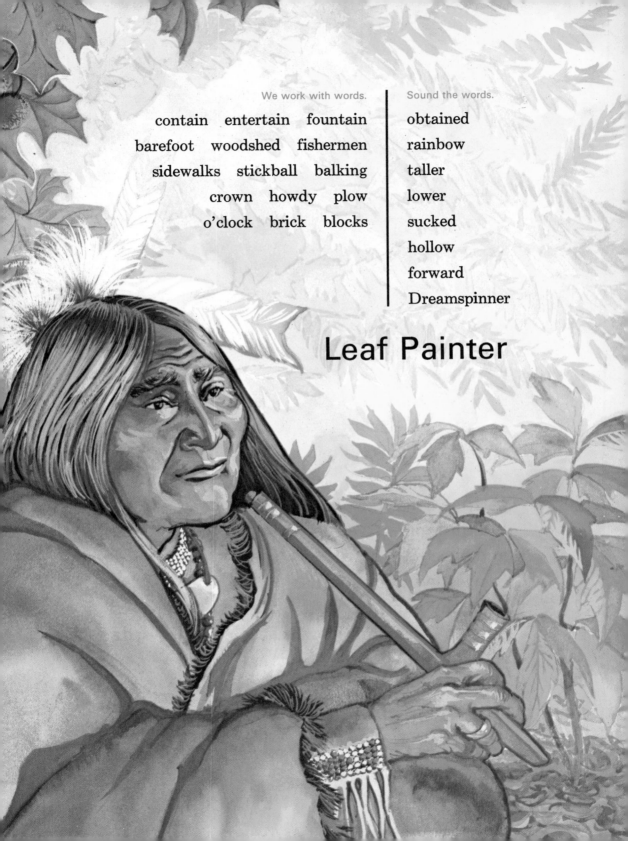

We work with words.

contain   entertain   fountain
barefoot   woodshed   fishermen
sidewalks   stickball   balking
crown   howdy   plow
o'clock   brick   blocks

Sound the words.

obtained
rainbow
taller
lower
sucked
hollow
forward
Dreamspinner

Leaf Painter

The late afternoon sun was just beginning
to slip behind the hills. The young Indians
sat around the fire with the old wise one
of the tribe, Dreamspinner.

The older men were out with their horses,
getting food for the winter ahead. The
Indian women were collecting fruit, roots,
and wood to help keep them through the
coming winter months.

As the sun fell behind the hills, the trees
seemed to dance with color like the
rainbow—brown, red, orange, yellow, and
still higher in the hills, the deep green
of the pine and spruce trees.

As evening came, the young people of the tribe moved closer to the fire where old Dreamspinner sat smoking his pipe. For a moment, there was only the still quiet that comes as the sun leaves for the day. Then the young brave, Swift Fox, turned to the wise one and asked, "Dreamspinner, why are all the trees so different? Some are yellow, others brown, and others almost red. And yet the pine and spruce trees are green and stay green all winter."

As Dreamspinner raised his head, the smoke rose slowly from his pipe and curled about his head. His eyes seemed far away, as if he were somewhere else. Then old Dreamspinner began his tale. His voice was low but easily understood.

"In the beginning was the Great Spirit, and the Great Spirit made everything. But there were many other spirits helping the Great Spirit. One of these spirits was called Growth Spirit. This spirit was the spirit of spring. Another was called Warm Spirit, the spirit of summer. The spirit that you asked about is Leaf Painter, the spirit of fall. And the last is Cold Spirit, the spirit of winter."

For a while Dreamspinner was silent. One of the young men laid wood on the fire, and the flames leaped higher. Then Dreamspinner spoke again. "But you asked me why the leaves of some trees are different and why certain trees stay green all year round. Now I will tell you.

"In the beginning, after Growth Spirit and Warm Spirit had finished their work, it came time for Leaf Painter, who was famous for the beauty of his work, to begin. It was time for him to finish the work started by Growth Spirit and Warm Spirit, time to make the hills beautiful. From the earth he obtained his color.

"From plants he took fruit, flowers, and roots. From the earth itself he made a bright brown. Certain fruit, flowers, and roots made a bright yellow. In the hollow of his hand he held the bright yellow. To this he added red earth to make orange. And from another fruit he obtained a deep blue like the night sky."

213

Dreamspinner seemed lost in another world as he continued. "Now you must remember that Leaf Painter was a spirit of great might and was well known for his works of beauty. He began quickly in the lower hills with his brown paint from the earth. With two strokes he was able to paint a whole tree, turning its leaves to golden brown. But there were many trees, and this work took several days.

"Next, Leaf Painter moved on to the taller trees. After much thought he decided that these should be a beautiful yellow, which would go well with the golden brown of the others. He took his yellow paint and worked several more days. This splash of yellow looked like our great star, the sun. Leaf Painter looked at his work and then moved on.

"The next trees were taller, and he decided to paint them a bright orange and red. For several more days he worked until the taller trees were covered with orange and red.

"Now only the trees high in the hills were left. Only the pine, the spruce, and the cedar were green. These, he decided, should be deep blue. But since he had worked several days, he chose to rest before climbing the steep hills.

"The next morning Leaf Painter went far up into the hills until he came to a group of pine trees. He put his hand on a tall pine, but the long, thin needles stuck his fingers. He stepped forward and tried again, and again the needles stuck his fingers. The pain was so great that he had to stop his work for the day. He could do no more.

"The next morning his hands felt better, and he decided to try the spruce tree. But again the needles hurt his fingers. He wondered how he would ever paint these trees. He decided to return to his home for a few days to think, to rest, and to care for his hands.

"During the night a soft rain fell, and in the morning when Leaf Painter awoke, he went out to get some water for his hurt hands. As he gazed upon the hills, he saw his rainbow of brown, yellow, orange, and red. And he saw drops of water that twinkled in the sun on the dark green pine, the spruce, and the cedar. Leaf Painter stood back. Never he he seen such beauty. He knew that this was right and beautiful. Leaf Painter decided they must stay as they are."

The burning fire was all that broke the quiet as Dreamspinner dropped his head and sucked on his pipe. Finally he raised his head and gazed into the darkness. The young Indians quietly rose to go to their homes, each to dream their own dreams.

Think about This:

1 Where might you hear a tale such as this told today?
2 Where do you think Dreamspinner first heard the tale he told to the young Indians?
3 What is different about the way these Indians lived from the way you live?

CITY HIGH, CITY LOW

pew drew chew

crew

soil loyal spoiled joyful

Boyd

groups soul thoughtful touched

Douglas

exercise excuse examined explore

expert

proved remove

movers

core bored restore

tore

Stebbins

figured piano

Avenue

Snakey

delivered

Mary

For Mary Ellis

Wanted: A Piano

Tomorrow is my sister's birthday," said Douglas Stebbins one day.

"Yes, I know," said Pete. "What does she want for a birthday present?"

"Oh, you know Mary Ellis," Doug sighed. "She still wants a piano more than anything. Mom sure would like to get one for her. But pianos cost way too much money."

"Aw, that's too bad," Pete said.

Then later that day, as Pete was looking for the funnies, he saw an article in the paper. He could hardly believe the words he saw — "Will give piano away. L. G. Boyd, 390 Central Avenue."

Pete tore out the article. Then he ran out of the house to find Doug.

"Wow!" Doug exclaimed. "But it must be a mistake—the article, I mean."

"Well, it won't do any harm to go find out about it," Pete said.

Doug raced toward Central Avenue with Pete close at his heels.

At the 390 Apartment House Doug pushed the button marked "Boyd." A man opened the door. "Yes?" he said.

Doug took off his cap. "Is this where a Mr. L. G. Boyd lives?" he asked.

"I'm Boyd," the man said. "What can I do for you?"

"I'm Douglas Stebbins," said Doug. Then he nodded toward Pete. "And this is Herbert Parnell Quinn. We've come about the piano you're giving away."

"We thought there might be some mistake about the piano being free," Pete said. "But Mary Ellis Stebbins wants a piano so bad we figured it wouldn't do any harm to find out about it."

Mr. Boyd led them into the living room. He questioned Douglas Stebbins about his sister, Mary Ellis, and then nodded toward the piano. "There it is, all yours."

"Wait until Mary Ellis sees that piano!" Doug beamed. "Her eyes will bulge right out of her head!"

"There's just one thing," Mr. Boyd said. "Are you sure you can pay expert movers to have the piano delivered to Mary Ellis?"

For a moment the boys couldn't say a word. They hadn't figured on having to pay for anything. They had thought the piano would be delivered for them.

"Exactly how much will it cost?" asked Doug, trying to sound as though the cost didn't really worry him.

"I can't tell exactly," replied Mr. Boyd. "Probably ten to twenty dollars."

After a while Pete found his tongue. "Oh, I guess it can be delivered all right. May we send for it tomorrow afternoon?"

"Certainly," said Mr. Boyd. "I won't be here, but the maid can let the moving crew in and show them the piano."

When they were out on the street, Doug groaned. "We should have known there was a catch. Where are we going to get ten or twenty dollars to move the piano?"

"We're not," said Pete. "It isn't a big piano. I bet we could move it if we got someone a little bigger to help. Maybe old Roy and Snakey can help us move it."

"It won't do any harm to try," Doug said. "Since Roy is pretty big, we could get him to dress in his dad's coveralls. Mr. Boyd's maid will think he looks exactly like a real expert moving man."

"Yeah, Snakey can dress up, too," Pete said. His eyes beamed. "Come on. Roy and Snakey don't know it yet, but we're all going to turn into expert piano movers!"

We work with words.

information section contraption
looms brooder soothing
gnaw hawk taught
future creatures moisture
heaven neighbor manner

Sound the words.

intersection
nook
paused
furniture
envelope
we'd
fretted
rumbling

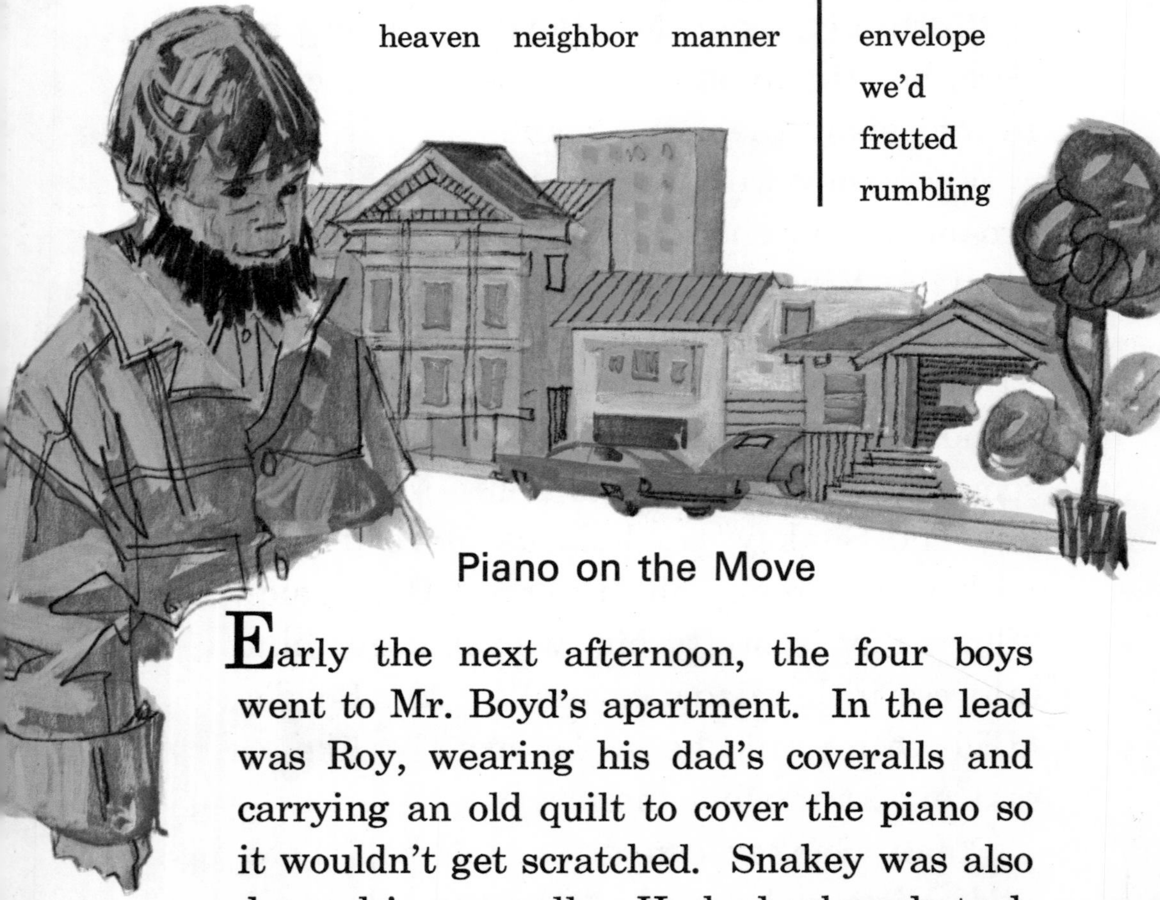

Piano on the Move

Early the next afternoon, the four boys went to Mr. Boyd's apartment. In the lead was Roy, wearing his dad's coveralls and carrying an old quilt to cover the piano so it wouldn't get scratched. Snakey was also dressed in coveralls. He had a beard stuck on his chin to make him look older, more like a real expert.

Roy and Snakey went to get the piano. Pete and Doug looked too young to be part of the moving crew, so they had to wait outside. They waited near a moving van that was being loaded with furniture from next door.

"I wish they'd come out," Doug fretted.

Then they heard a rumbling sound and the sound of squeaky rollers as Roy and Snakey pushed the piano onto the sidewalk. The maid followed them out. But when she saw the moving van, she went back inside. That must have made her think the boys were a real expert moving crew.

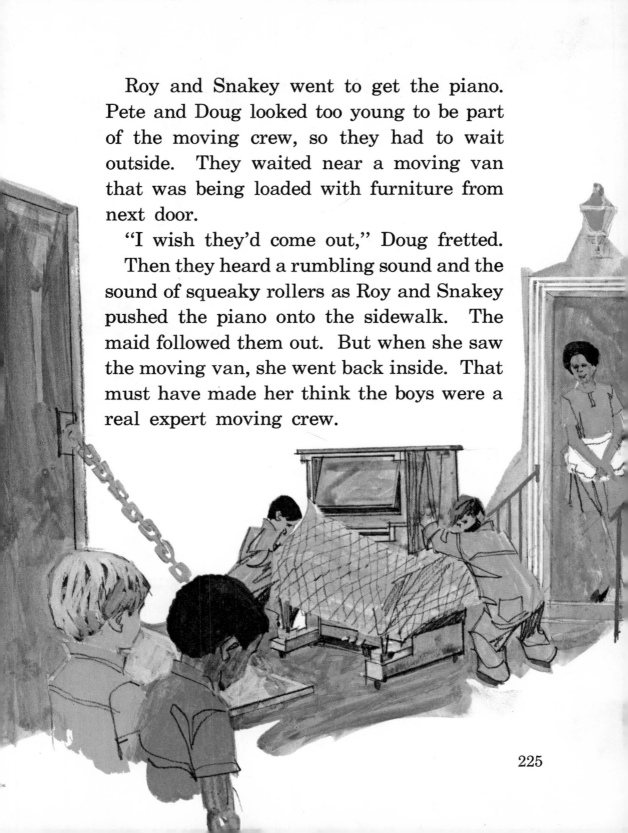

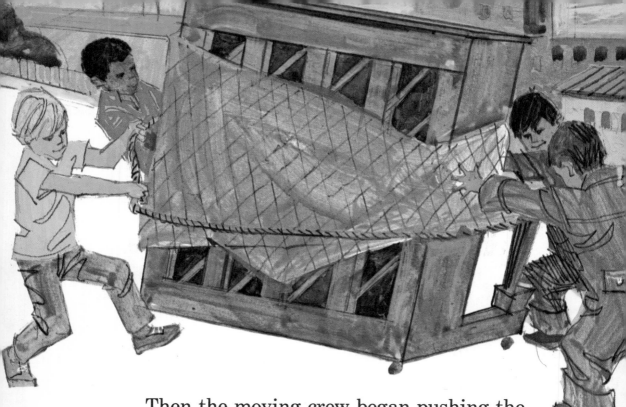

Then the moving crew began pushing the piano down the sidewalk. When they had gone halfway down the block, Snakey paused and tore the beard off his chin.

"We'd better get ready for that steep hill down Central Avenue," he said. Then he tied a thick cord around the piano.

"Doug, you and Pete stay in back and pull on this cord as hard as you can to keep the piano from rolling too fast," said Snakey. "Roy and I'll keep her steady in front. When the traffic light is green, we'll head down the hill toward the intersection."

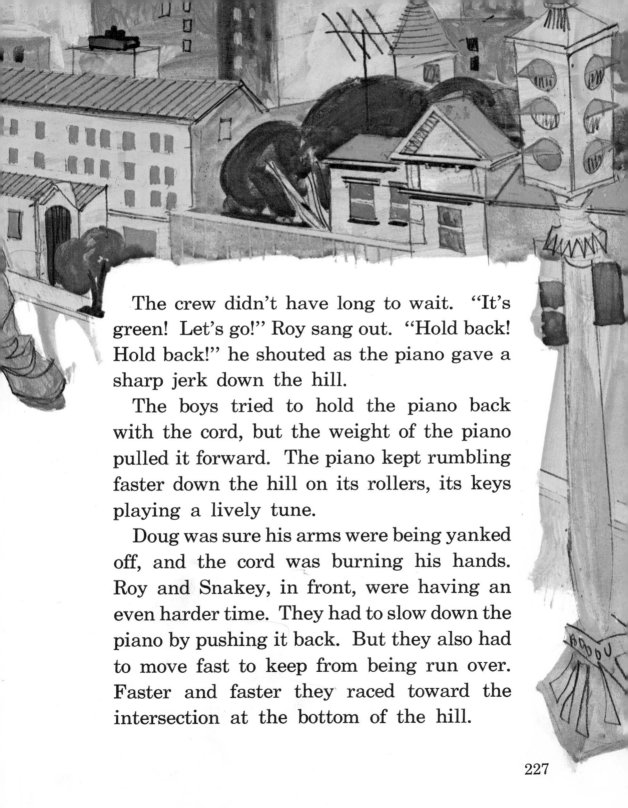

The crew didn't have long to wait. "It's green! Let's go!" Roy sang out. "Hold back! Hold back!" he shouted as the piano gave a sharp jerk down the hill.

The boys tried to hold the piano back with the cord, but the weight of the piano pulled it forward. The piano kept rumbling faster down the hill on its rollers, its keys playing a lively tune.

Doug was sure his arms were being yanked off, and the cord was burning his hands. Roy and Snakey, in front, were having an even harder time. They had to slow down the piano by pushing it back. But they also had to move fast to keep from being run over. Faster and faster they raced toward the intersection at the bottom of the hill.

227

What if the light wasn't exactly right? They wouldn't be able to stop the piano before it went into the intersection.

But the light stayed green until the boys got across the intersection. Then halfway down the next block the hill was gone. So was the sidewalk! From there on, the crew had to pull the piano through traffic.

The boys finally arrived at Doug's house. "Did Mary Ellis and Mom get back yet?" Doug asked a neighbor standing nearby.

"No," replied the neighbor, "but they should be coming soon. You'd better hurry and get the piano inside. It's exactly four o'clock and almost time for the party."

Two of the neighbors helped carry the piano to a nook in the living room.

"Now, what can we do to surprise Mary Ellis?" Doug asked the other boys.

The four boys put their heads together and came up with a plan. Then, just when Mary Ellis and her mother arrived, Pete struck the keys of the piano.

Mary Ellis paused at the door. Her face lit up as she gazed into the living room. "Where did the piano come from?" she asked as she rushed over to touch the keys.

"How would we know that?" said Doug.

"Quit joking, Doug," Mary Ellis fretted. "Where did it come from? Is it for me?"

"Naw," answered Doug. "It was delivered here by mistake. A moving van arrived, and I told the movers not to unpack that piece of furniture. They didn't listen, but I told them it was a mistake."

"Furniture!" cried Mary Ellis. "A piano isn't a piece of furniture!" Mary Ellis frowned and shut her eyes.

"What's this?" her mother said as she took an envelope from the top of the piano. "This envelope has your name on it."

Mary Ellis paused a moment, looking at the envelope. Then she tore it open and read softly, "Surprise! Surprise! The piano is for you. Happy Birthday, Mary Ellis."

For a whole minute she stood there in the nook, looking first at the note and then at the piano. She looked very unhappy.

"Aw, for Pete's sake, Mary Ellis," Doug groaned. He turned to his mother. "Mom, doesn't she like the piano?"

"Like it? Why, of course she likes it!" Mother said.

Mary Ellis turned toward Doug. Her eyes were shining. "I love it," she said.

feather   tractor   sugar

favor

mirrors   sorrow   berry   narrow

borrow

report   comfort   recorded   form

formed

worst   workmen   housework

worse

tracking   licked   haystack

stickball

joined   royal   points   coin

soil

thoughtful   soul   youth

touched

Miguel's

tomato

favorite

Rooftop Secret

At last spring had come to Miguel's city. The sunshine felt warm on Miguel's face and arms. "It's good that spring has come," Miguel thought. "Now Carlos and I can play stickball again. But best of all, I can go to my favorite place. Even Carlos doesn't know about it."

Miguel's favorite place was the roof of his apartment house. He could sit there and see for blocks around. It was private there. The noise of the city seemed far away.

Late one afternoon Miguel climbed the steps to his favorite place and watched the busy traffic below. Soon the warm sun made him thirsty.

"I wish I had a big juicy tomato," he thought. How Miguel did love tomatoes!

When the sun began to set, Miguel turned to go down the steps. Suddenly he stopped. At his feet was something small and green. It was a plant, growing on his roof! Miguel put his face close to it. He smelled it and gently touched its leaves.

"It smells like tomatoes!" he thought. "How did it get here? Will it grow big and have ripe juicy tomatoes?" Miguel wanted to care for it—it was his. What a wonderful secret it would be!

Every day after that Miguel had no time to play stickball. After school he hurried home to see his plant. One day some of its leaves had turned yellow. The next day the plant looked worse. Its leaves were crisp, and they broke off when he touched them.

"What is wrong?" Miguel questioned. "How can I find out what to do?"

The next day, to Miguel's surprise, his teacher spoke to the class about plants. "The roots must live in rich soil," she said as she gently lifted the roots of the plant she was showing. "Plants get thirsty and must have sunshine and water."

"That's what is wrong with my plant," thought Miguel. "It needs some soil."

After school the wind was blowing hard. Pieces of paper and trash sailed along the sidewalk. Mr. Jones was picking up some of the paper when Miguel came by.

"Hello, Miguel," said Mr. Jones. "I'll pay you a quarter if you'll do me a favor and pick up this trash for me."

Miguel didn't really want to take the time to do anyone a favor. But then he saw the wooden boxes Mr. Jones had in front of his store.

"May I have one of those wooden boxes instead of money?" Miguel asked.

"All right," said Mr. Jones. "But I've never met a boy who wanted a wooden box instead of money."

Miguel picked up all the paper and put it in the trash can. Then Mr. Jones gave him a box and two juicy apples.

Miguel hurried home. He passed the door of his apartment and ran to the roof. His plant looked even worse.

"Now I have a box," Miguel thought. "But where can I get some rich soil?"

Then he remembered. Last Saturday he and Carlos had watched machines in a nearby lot pushing up soil for trucks to haul away. That lot had rich, black dirt!

"I sure would like to have some of that dirt," Miguel said to himself. "I'll go see if anyone is there."

The foreman and the construction workers were still at work when Miguel arrived.

"Is it okay if I take some dirt?" Miguel asked the foreman.

"Take all you want," the foreman said.

Miguel filled his small can with dirt and carried it up to the roof. But when he put the dirt into his box, it covered only the bottom. "That's shallow. I need to haul a lot more dirt," he thought.

Quickly he ran down to his apartment. "Mamma," he called. "May I borrow your wash bucket?"

"You may borrow it if you bring it back," said his mother.

Miguel hurried back to the lot and filled the bucket with dirt. He got awfully tired as he carried the heavy bucket home. But he now had deep soil for his plant.

Gently Miguel lifted his plant from the crack in the roof. He laid its long root in the soil and covered it.

That night it rained, and the next day Miguel discovered his plant standing very straight and tall. It had even formed two new leaves. How pleased Miguel was!

When summer vacation came, Miguel had plenty of time to play stickball. He helped Mamma, and every day he watched his plant grow. Soon it grew some yellow flowers. And in each flower a small, green ball slowly formed. As the days passed by, the green balls grew bigger and bigger. Before long the sun and rain turned them red.

Now there were many ripe tomatoes on the plant. They were all big and juicy, and they made Miguel thirsty! He picked one and sucked its warm red juice.

Then Miguel picked the biggest red tomato he could find. "This one is for Mamma," he said with a proud feeling.

"Mamma! Mamma! Look what I grew," Miguel shouted as he came into the kitchen. Then he told all about his secret.

Mamma was pleased. She cut the tomato in thin pieces and put them on the table.

All summer Miguel picked tomatoes from his plant. Before the last tomato was gone, Miguel was already making plans for the next summer. He planned to grow a whole garden of vegetables on the roof. Crisp green cucumbers, beans, lettuce, and ripe red tomatoes!

We work with words.

serve　circle　curds　birth

frosty　tossed　softer

thoughtful　tough　ghostly

impossible　supply　tables

lovely　colors　dozen

Sight word.

Ramón

Sound the words.

scurrying

crossed

ghastly

ladies

shoved

Bobo

budge

Straight Up to Grandmother's

The first time Rosa said that her grandmother lived straight up, Carlos said, "Ha! Does your grandmother live in a balloon? Or maybe she lives on the moon? Come on, Rosa. Nobody lives straight up. Ha!"

But the joke was on Carlos because Rosa's grandmother did live straight up, straight up above Rosa's apartment on the third floor.

From her window on the third floor Rosa could hear the hustle and bustle of cars and trucks in the street below. She could even hear the people on the sidewalk laugh when the cars were quiet and she was listening very carefully.

Straight up in the tall apartment building, behind the shiny row of windows one floor down from the top, was her grandmother's apartment. From her grandmother's window, Rosa could still see cars on the street far below. But she couldn't hear their horns, and the people looked like tiny insects scurrying along the sidewalk.

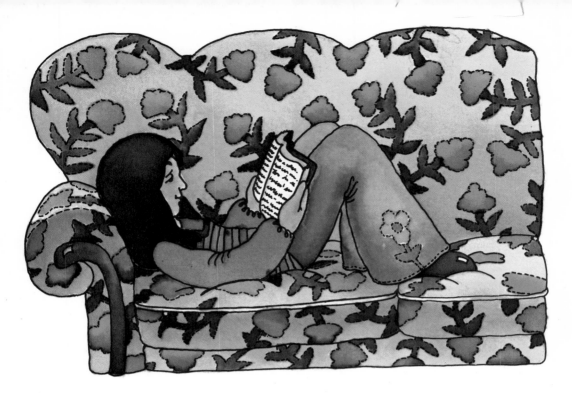

The best thing about Rosa's grandmother's apartment was that it was easy to get to. Usually it took Rosa about a minute. That is, most of the time it took about a minute. Then there were days like today.

Rosa read for a while. She watched television for a while. She looked out the window at a pigeon for a while. "Hmmm," she said. Finally she called to her mother in the next room. "Mother, I think I'll visit Grandmother. Call when you want me." Out the door she went, across the hall, and into the elevator.

The elevator climbed to the next floor, and the doors swished open. A short lady with a dog almost as tall as Rosa got on. Rosa looked at the dog and smiled. The dog looked at Rosa and wagged his tail. "Good dog," Rosa said. The dog said nothing, though he looked as if he wanted to as he gave Rosa a lick on the face.

"My dog's name is Bobo," the short lady said. "He'll bark when we reach our floor, but he won't budge before. Wait and see."

"Oh," Rosa said because she didn't know what else to say. Then she added, "I guess he's a smart dog."

"He certainly is," the short lady said.

Rosa watched the lights blink as the elevator climbed. Then the elevator stopped again, and the doors swished open.

Three women and a fat man stepped in. Bobo moved away from them and sat on Rosa's feet. Rosa, the short lady, and Bobo were shoved to the back. The three ladies stood in a row in front of them. The fat man stood at the very front of the elevator.

Rosa watched the lights blink again as the elevator began to climb.

It had gone up only two floors when it stopped again. A young man with red hair waited a moment as the fat man moved back to make room, and then he walked in. He was holding a fluffy yellow cat wearing a gold collar. A blue ribbon dangled from the collar. It said, "First Prize."

"Wow!" Rosa thought. "What a cat!"

The short lady next to Rosa looked down and said, "This is our floor. Come, Bobo."

243

Suddenly Bobo barked, and in the crowded elevator it was a very loud bark. The yellow cat, who had not even seen Bobo in the back of the elevator, leaped up and came down on the head of the fat man. At that moment the elevator doors opened. Out darted Bobo after the cat. And out ran the young man with red hair, yelling, "Stop! Stop!"

"How ghastly!" one of the women said. "I just don't think animals should ride on elevators."

"Nor do I," the fat man said with a snort.

As for Rosa, she thought it had been very funny, but she didn't say so as the elevator climbed three more floors and stopped. The ladies and the fat man walked off the elevator.

Before the doors swished shut, a man with a beard and the most beautiful woman Rosa had ever seen walked in. Both of them smiled at Rosa and then began to sing. When they stopped singing, the elevator seemed very quiet.

"That was very nice," Rosa said, though for the life of her she could not figure out why they were singing.

"I'm glad you liked it. Tonight we sing at a party for the mayor," the man said as the elevator arrived at his floor and the doors opened. "That room right there," he said, pointing across the hall. They began to sing again as they crossed the hall.

"Gee!" Rosa said aloud as the elevator started again. "This must be the longest elevator trip ever."

Rosa watched the lights blink as the elevator climbed from floor to floor. Finally it reached her grandmother's floor and stopped. But the doors didn't open. "Oh, no!" Rosa said.

With a small jerk the elevator started down. Rosa stuck her hands in her pockets and sighed. Halfway to the bottom floor the elevator stopped again. This time two girls, one with golden hair and one with brown hair, walked into the elevator.

"How did the circus go last night?" the girl with golden hair asked.

"Not very well," her friend answered. "My foot slipped on the high swings."

"It's a good thing you and Ramón use a net," the girl with golden hair said.

"Oh, but we didn't use one last night," her friend answered.

Rosa's eyes grew big as she listened.

"Tell me what happened!" the girl with golden hair said quickly.

"Well," the girl replied, "Somehow Ramón swung down and—"

The elevator reached the bottom floor, the doors opened, and the two girls started to walk away. Rosa just couldn't keep quiet any longer. "Don't get off! Please tell me what happened!"

"What?" the girls said together.

"Oh, I see. We can't leave you up in the air—or me, either," the girl with brown hair added with a laugh. "We'll ride back up with you. Let's see, where was I?"

"You were saying something about Ramón," Rosa said.

"Oh, I remember. Well, Ramón swung down and caught me at the very last minute. You should have heard the people shout. They thought it was part of the show. Say," the girl said, just as the elevator reached Grandmother's floor, "would you like to go to the circus?"

"I sure would!" Rosa answered.

"How many people are in your family?" the girl asked.

"Mother, Dad, and Grandmother," Rosa answered.

"You left someone out, didn't you?" the girl with golden hair said.

"But I won't," the other girl said. "Here is a pass for you—and three more for your family."

"Thank you!" Rosa said as the doors opened. She crossed the hall to her grandmother's apartment.

"Rosa!" her grandmother said. "How nice to see you. I'm glad our family is in the same apartment building. The only trouble is that you don't get to travel to see me, and you don't get to meet all the different people you would meet on a trip."

"Oh, that's all right," Rosa said. "I like having you here."

marks stars charges marched

airy stairway fairly

endure cure measure

chore shore score

merry sorrow carries

dart

repairmen

measuring

explore

narrow

tunnel

reported

thousand

alligators

cockroaches

Amazing
Underground City

In 1888 a terrible snowstorm hit New York City. Tall poles snapped, and electric wires fell into the street. People were killed by electric shock. Some were killed by the falling poles. And nearly a thousand died in the fires that broke out.

The mayor saw that he must do something to make his city a safe place to live. He asked electricians to put electric wires safely underground. Then the mayor sent men out to take down the wooden poles.

These electric wires were the beginning of America's amazing underground city in New York. Today the narrow streets and the sidewalks hide more than four million miles of wire. In some places there are so many wires and pipes that two fingers cannot be pushed between them.

By 1900, New York City had a different problem. The city was growing too fast. Nearly a million people were jammed into apartment buildings. Traffic could hardly move in the narrow streets. Something had to be done about the traffic and about the city water supply.

It was decided that the city water supply should be stored below ground and carried through tunnels to the people. Water Tunnel Number One, measuring ten miles long, took ten years to build. It carries most of the 375 million gallons of water used by the people in New York City each day.

Something was done about the traffic on the narrow streets, too. A tunnel was built below the streets so that people could travel quickly to work. The subway track, measuring more than two hundred miles, was laid inside the huge tunnel. Today subway trains dart below the city from one end to the other. And the huge tunnels under the rivers bring cars, trucks, and trains into New York City each day.

But even the people in subway trains do not see all that lies below New York City. For years, repairmen working below the city have been surprised to find many strange things in some of these tunnels.

Workers have reported seeing a nest of ten thousand mice in one of the tunnels. Alligators that measure nearly eight feet long have been found in some of the wet, warm tunnels. Cats that can leap twenty feet, huge rats as big as cats, and flying cockroaches that measure six inches have been reported to live underground.

Other things below New York City are just as amazing. Repairmen have discovered parts of old ships, trunks full of old coins, and many valuable stones here. Today the lower levels of a city store, a school, a police station, and even the lower levels of a hospital may be found underground.

Alligators, cockroaches, rats, stones, and stores. Amazing! Some people explore outer space. Others explore the deep earth. How would you like to explore America's amazing underground city?

We work with words.

retire firefly admire
warble wart warn
hare dared share
dolphin elephants autograph
searching pear appears

Sound the words.

admired
warning
shared
trophy
Earl
comet
sneakers
Alex
shuffled
roller
champ
atomic

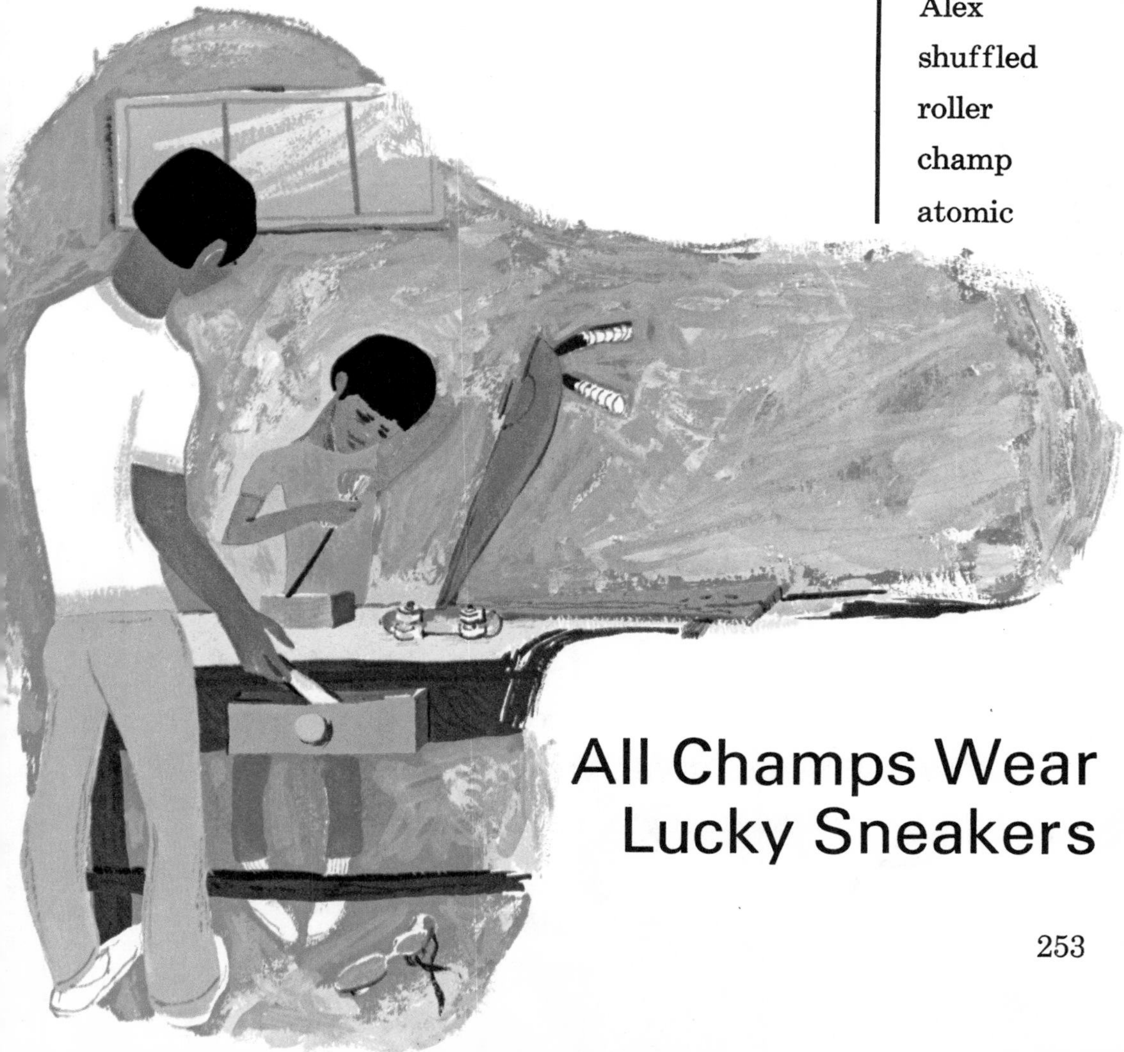

All Champs Wear Lucky Sneakers

Good-bye, Mom. So long, Champ," Alex called as he drove away with Dad on his way to summer camp.

"Champ!" Earl gulped. He sure hoped it turned out that way.

Today was the day of the race. Earl just had to win! He admired his older brother, Alex, who was a champ at almost everything he tried. And Earl wanted to show Alex he could be a champ, too.

Alex was like Dad, full of talk and sure of himself. Earl was like Mom, quiet and shy. But when Alex came home, Earl hoped to have a trophy to show him.

"How about pancakes for breakfast this morning?" Earl's mother asked.

"Okay, but hurry, Mom," Earl said. "I can hardly wait to take the Red Comet to the race track."

Earl and his father had built the Red Comet in the basement of their apartment building. The Comet was painted bright red with a blazing yellow comet tail painted down each side. Even when it was still, the Red Comet seemed to be racing.

Who would believe it had been made from a wooden crate and the wheels off his old roller skates? The Red Comet looked like a winner. Earl hoped he was one, too.

While Mom made the pancakes, Earl went to the bedroom that he shared with Alex.

"I wish there was a way to make sure to win," Earl mumbled.

He ran his fingers over the gold trophy Alex had won in a track meet last summer. He remembered how proud Dad had been. "Aw," Alex had said, "it wasn't me as much as my lucky sneakers."

Earl opened the closet, and there on the floor lay Alex's lucky sneakers. Earl took off his own sneakers and put his feet into Alex's. They were too long.

He shuffled around in them for a minute, then stuffed the toes with paper and tried them on again. He looked in the mirror and admired his toes. "Not bad," Earl mumbled. "I'll wear Alex's sneakers. Then nothing can stop me from winning."

"Why are you wearing Alex's sneakers?" Mom asked at breakfast. "Aren't they too big for you?"

"They were," Earl said. "But I stuffed them with paper. They'll be okay."

"Okay for what?" his mother asked.

"For the race," Earl said. "I'm wearing them for luck."

"It doesn't matter what you wear," said his mother. "You make your own luck."

Just then someone knocked at the door.

"That's Lenny," Earl called as he ran to the door.

Lenny was only a few months older than Earl. But he was nearly a head taller.

"Come on in," Earl said. Then Earl shared his pancakes with his very best friend.

After breakfast Mom said to Earl, "Why don't you wear your own sneakers?"

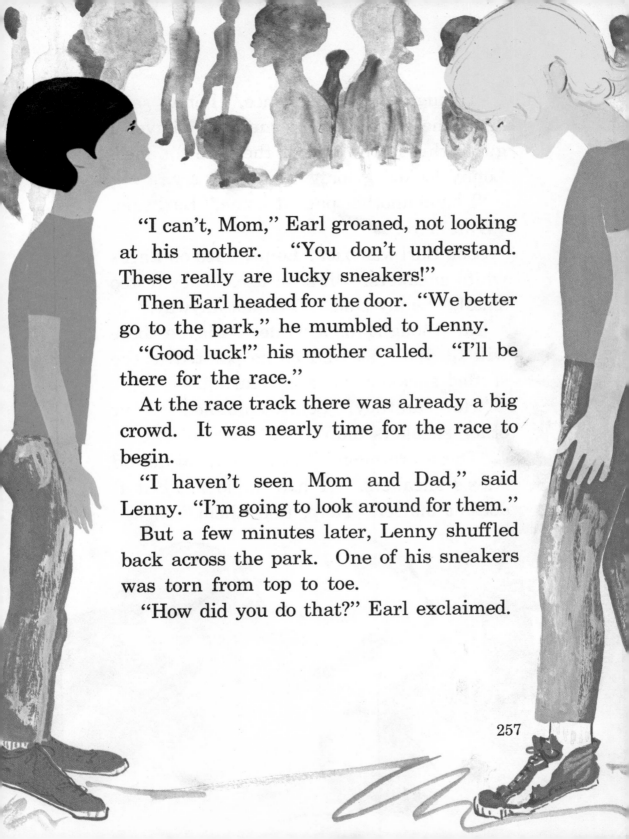

"I can't, Mom," Earl groaned, not looking at his mother. "You don't understand. These really are lucky sneakers!"

Then Earl headed for the door. "We better go to the park," he mumbled to Lenny.

"Good luck!" his mother called. "I'll be there for the race."

At the race track there was already a big crowd. It was nearly time for the race to begin.

"I haven't seen Mom and Dad," said Lenny. "I'm going to look around for them."

But a few minutes later, Lenny shuffled back across the park. One of his sneakers was torn from top to toe.

"How did you do that?" Earl exclaimed.

"I caught it on the fence," Lenny said. "And these are the only sneakers I have. I guess this is the end of the race for me." Lenny looked gloomy enough to cry.

"I have another pair at home," Earl said. "Wait here!"

Soon Earl was back. Lenny tried on Earl's white sneakers. "It's no use. They're too small," Lenny said. "Thanks anyway."

Earl thought for a while. "Maybe these will fit you," he said as he pointed to the stuffed sneakers he was wearing.

"How can they?" Lenny mumbled. "Your other sneakers didn't."

"These are bigger," Earl said, taking off Alex's sneakers. "I had an idea. But it doesn't matter. Here, take them."

Suddenly the warning whistle blew. Then a loud voice called out, "All racers to the starting line!"

Quickly the boys tied their sneakers. Then Earl heard his mother's voice.

"Remember, Earl," she called. "You make your own luck!"

Earl had that tight feeling deep in his stomach as he hurried with the Comet to the starting line. He just had to win! But what chance did he have without Alex's lucky sneakers?

"Ready!" the judge gave his warning. Earl braced one foot against the Red Comet.

"On your mark!" the judge called.

"Go!" shouted the judge.

The racers charged forward with a grind, and the crowds cheered. Earl saw one racer swoop past him, then another, and then it was Lenny with his Green Bug.

"It's the lucky sneakers!" Earl panted. "Without them, I'm not going to win!"

Then Earl heard a voice shouting above all the others. "Come on, Champ! Come on, Earl. You can do it!"

His heart leaped. Was that his mother's voice? Mom, who was shy and never raised her voice if she could help it?

"Come on, Champ!" Mom yelled. "You can do it! It's up to you!"

With a swift shove, Earl bolted forward. Another shove and another, he struggled on ahead. The Red Comet passed one racer after another. At the halfway mark, Earl swung around for the second half of the race. What did it matter whose sneakers he wore? He was like a flashing comet!

Earl was breathing hard. He seemed to be racing on atomic power as he shot farther ahead. In a moment he was in the lead. Then, racing at top speed, Earl cut through the ribbon at the end of the track. And a shout went up from the crowd.

"The winner!" exclaimed the judge as he raised Earl's hand. Then the crowd cheered as the judge gave him a trophy and a pair of roller skates.

Mom gripped Earl's shoulder. "Well done, Champ!" she exclaimed.

Earl laughed and wiggled his toes in his own white sneakers. "I guess all champs wear lucky sneakers," he said.

Think about This:

1 What did Mom say to Earl that he finally learned was right?
2 Why was Earl finally able to win the race when at first it seemed he would lose it?
3 Why do you suppose it was so important to Earl to become a champ?
4 What could Earl have made with old roller skates besides the Red Comet?

THE WISE AND THE FOOLISH

surely pure secure lure

hire tireless sire inquire

flare squarely scares

squirt curds alert

larch pardon marched

fountains entertain contain

feather beggar tractor

excitement exercising exact

Sight words.

anxious honest mysteriously

Sound the words.

purest

empire

dared

urged

guards

captain

Emperor

excitedly

faithful

invisible

magnificent

imagine

The Emperor's
New Clothes

Many years ago there lived an emperor who had great interest in fine new clothes. He paid nearly all his money in order to be well-dressed in public.

One morning two strangers arrived at the Emperor's palace. They told the Emperor they could make the most beautiful cloth he could imagine.

"Not only are the colors and the patterns beautiful," the men told the Emperor, "but clothes made of our cloth are magic. The clothes are invisible to anyone who is not fit for his office or is too stupid."

"Those would be fine clothes to have," thought the Emperor. "By wearing them, I could find out which men in my empire are not fit for the office they hold. I could tell the wise from the foolish."

So the Emperor gave the two weavers a great deal of money to begin their work at weaving cloth.

The men smiled mysteriously as they set up their looms. Then they went to work, pretending to be weaving cloth. But they had nothing at all on their looms. The men kept asking the Emperor for his fine silks and his purest, most shiny gold. These they put into their own pockets, then worked far into the night at their empty looms.

"I wonder how the weavers are proceeding with my new clothes!" thought the Emperor. He remembered that anyone who was foolish or not fit for his office would not be able to see the wonderful cloth.

"I will test my honest Prime Minister!" thought the Emperor. "I will send him to the weavers to see the cloth."

So the honest Prime Minister went to the room where the two men sat working at the empty looms.

"Goodness!" thought the Prime Minister, opening his eyes wide. "I can't see the cloth! It must be invisible!"

But the Prime Minister said none of this aloud. Instead he thought, "Is it possible I am not faithful to my office? No, No! It certainly would never do for me to admit I can't see the cloth."

"Well, sir," said the weavers. "You have not praised our weaving!"

"It's lovely! Magnificent!" the old Prime Minister said excitedly as he looked at the empty looms.

The weavers smiled mysteriously. They named the colors of the cloth, one by one, and told about the patterns and the purest silks they had used. The Prime Minister listened carefully and then reported their words exactly to the Emperor.

Later, the anxious Emperor sent his most faithful Captain of the Guards to see if the cloth would soon be finished.

The Captain, too, praised the cloth he could not see. He told the weavers he liked the patterns, the beautiful colors, and the purest silks. He did not wish to appear stupid or foolish.

"It's more magnificent than you can ever imagine!" the Captain told the Emperor.

Now everyone in the empire was talking excitedly about the wonderful cloth. At last the old Prime Minister and the Captain urged the Emperor to see it for himself. They were anxious to see what the Emperor would have to say.

Soon the Emperor, his Prime Minister, and the Captain of the Guards went to visit the weavers. The two weavers appeared to be busy weaving. But they hadn't the smallest bit of cloth in sight.

"Isn't it magnificent!" cried the Prime Minister and the Captain of the Guards.

"What's this?" thought the Emperor. "I don't see a thing! Am I stupid? This is terrible! Am I not honest and faithful and fit to be Emperor of my empire?"

At last, so he would not appear foolish, the Emperor said aloud, "Oh, it is indeed beautiful! I am very pleased!"

Then everyone urged the Emperor to have clothes made of this wonderful cloth.

"You will be dressed in a becoming manner for the great parade tomorrow!" cried the Captain of the Guards.

All night the weavers worked, pretending to make the Emperor's new clothes.

268

The next morning, the weavers whistled and hummed as they pretended to dress the Emperor. They snapped one invisible snap after the other as they fitted the clothes on the Emperor and turned him from side to side in front of the mirror.

"My, how becoming! How well the weavers have fitted you!" everyone said.

"The parade is ready to begin," called the Captain of the Guards.

"Well, I am dressed!" said the Emperor as he marched excitedly in front of the mirror. "Don't my new clothes hang well?" He wanted it to appear as if he were looking very carefully at the way his fine new clothes had been fitted.

Two honest boys were asked to carry the Emperor's train. Mysteriously they reached down to the floor, pretending to pick it up. The boys dared not let it be known that they saw no train at all.

And so the Emperor marched in the parade for the whole empire to see. And everyone who watched cried aloud, "See the Emperor's new clothes! Look how becoming. See how very well they fit."

Not a person dared to say there were no clothes on the Emperor as he was proceeding down the street in the parade. To admit that would have meant they were not fit for office, or were very stupid.

Then suddenly one child's eyes grew wide when the Emperor marched by. "The Emperor has nothing on!" cried the little child excitedly.

"Oh, don't mind my boy!" said the boy's anxious father. "He knows no better!"

But one person whispered to another what the little child had said. "The Emperor has nothing on." And soon all the people were shouting, "He has nothing on!"

The Emperor had a strange feeling, for it seemed to him that they were right. But he thought, "It's too late now. I must go on with the parade."

So the Emperor carried himself in a proud manner, and the young boys walked along behind him carrying the train which was not there at all.

Think about This:

1 Why do you suppose it was a child who said what others would not admit?
2 Which people in the story were foolish?
3 How do you know that the Prime Minister was not really honest?

271

In My New Clothing

In my new clothing
> I feel so different
> I must
Look like someone else

by Basho

muddled squeaked spoiled rested

written stiffen brighten

graceful cheerful playful hopeful

prisoner fiddler brooder

collection suggestion information

excuse tease case

repeated

brightened

thoughtful

reporter

contraption

raise

Rafferty

Alsop

plastic

howdy

gradually

Blue Faces
and Star Bones

A Strange Contraption

Rafferty left *The Times* press car under a tree and stood looking at the old house. Then he went into the yard and carefully climbed the creaky steps.

Alfred Alsop came out on the porch to meet him. "Howdy do," he said.

"I'm Rafferty of *The Times*," said the reporter.

"Rafferty?" Mr. Alsop said.

"I'm a reporter," Rafferty replied. "I was called and told that an airplane had crashed around here."

Mr. Alsop looked thoughtful and shook his head slowly.

"No," he said. Then he repeated, "Noooo."

The screen door squeaked and Mrs. Alsop came out. "Howdy," she said.

Rafferty repeated the information for Mrs. Alsop while Mr. Alsop rested against the screen door looking thoughtful. "Noooo," Mrs. Alsop said, shaking her head. "Nothing like that crashed near here."

"I guess there's been a mistake," said Rafferty as he turned to go. "Lots of times a reporter gets the wrong information in these matters. Someone reported that an airplane came down in your flat field this morning, leaving a trail of fire."

Mrs. Alsop's face gradually brightened. "Ohhhhhh!" she said. "Yes, it did, but it didn't crash. Besides, it couldn't be an airplane. That is, it doesn't have wings on it."

"What?" Rafferty said. "An airplane came down? And it didn't have wings?"

"Yes," Mrs. Alsop said. "It's out there in the barn now. It belongs to some folks who have come to pay us a visit."

This information, Rafferty thought, began to smell like news again.

"Oh, a helicopter," he said.

Mrs. Alsop shook her head. "Noooooo. I don't think it is. It doesn't have any of those fans. But you can go out to the barn and have a look if it matters to you. Take him out, Alfred. Watch out for the mud while you're crossing the yard."

"Come on," Mr. Alsop said. "I'd like to look at the contraption again myself."

Rafferty followed along as Mr. Alsop led the way to the barn, crossing the yard on a walk.

"Got a lot of fine chickens this year," Mr. Alsop said. "Very fine chickens," he repeated. Then he became thoughtful again. "Do you think chickens will do very well up on a star, Mr. Rafferty?" he asked.

"On a what?" said Rafferty.

"Up on a star."

Mr. Alsop's barn door squeaked as he tried bending the latch to open it. "Sticks," he said. Rafferty helped with the latch, and together they slid the door open. As soon as he looked inside the barn, Rafferty knew he had a story.

The contraption looked like a big plastic balloon only half-filled. It was round on top, and its flat bottom rested in a circle on the floor. It was just small enough to go through the barn door.

"Mr. Alsop," Rafferty said, "you didn't build this thing, did you?"

Mr. Alsop laughed. "Oh, noooo. I didn't build it. I wouldn't know how to build one of those things. It belongs to some friends of ours who arrived in it. Goodness, no, I wouldn't even know how to fly one."

"Just who are these friends, Mr. Alsop?" Rafferty asked.

"Well, it sounds funny," Mr. Alsop said, looking thoughtful, "but I don't exactly know. They don't talk so very good. They don't talk at all. All we can get out of them is that their name is something about bending iron with a hammer."

Rafferty had been walking in a circle around the contraption, gradually drawing closer to it. He suddenly bumped into a something he couldn't see. "Ouch!" he said as he rubbed his chin.

"Oh, I forgot to tell you, Mr. Rafferty," Mr. Alsop said. "It's got a gadget on it that won't let you get near, some kind of screen or wall—invisible like—something you can't see. That's to keep people away from it."

"Mr. Alsop, where are these friends of yours now?" Rafferty asked.

"Ohhhhhh, they're over at the house," Mr. Alsop said. "You can see them if you want. But I think you'll find it pretty hard to talk to them."

"Let's go," Rafferty mumbled as he backed gradually away from the plastic balloon.

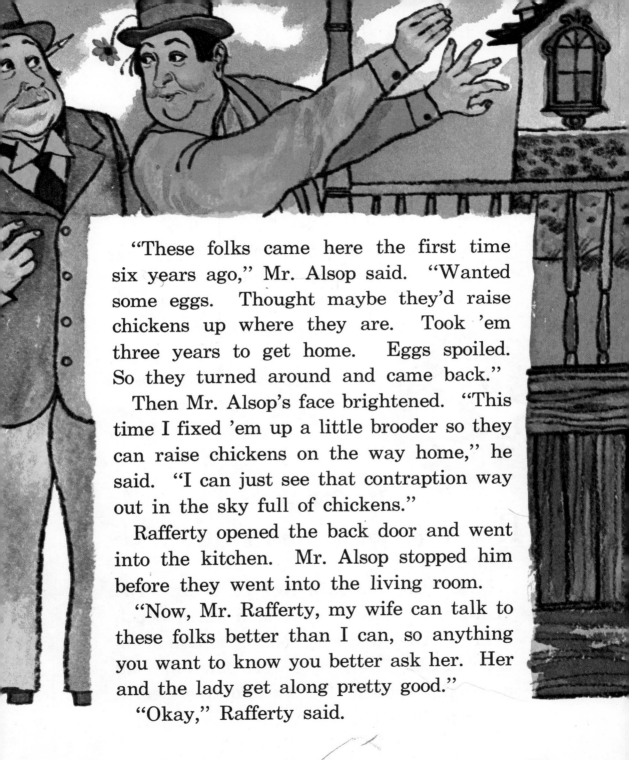

"These folks came here the first time six years ago," Mr. Alsop said. "Wanted some eggs. Thought maybe they'd raise chickens up where they are. Took 'em three years to get home. Eggs spoiled. So they turned around and came back."

Then Mr. Alsop's face brightened. "This time I fixed 'em up a little brooder so they can raise chickens on the way home," he said. "I can just see that contraption way out in the sky full of chickens."

Rafferty opened the back door and went into the kitchen. Mr. Alsop stopped him before they went into the living room.

"Now, Mr. Rafferty, my wife can talk to these folks better than I can, so anything you want to know you better ask her. Her and the lady get along pretty good."

"Okay," Rafferty said.

worrying marrying drying prying

drier fairies merriest

hopefully bravely neatly

exercising chasing muddled

linger tangled jingle

scolded molding boldly

purely feature cures creature

antennae

scurrying

craziest

politely

puzzled

finger

folded

creatures

Ethel

flexible

perhaps

skeletons

camera

The Star Ducks

Rafferty pushed Mr. Alsop gently into the living room.

Mrs. Alsop sat in a rocking chair. The visitors sat side by side on a small bench nearby. They had long flexible antennae on their heads. Their faces were pale blue and as blank as paper. Their round eyes seemed to be painted on.

"Mr. Rafferty," Mrs. Alsop said, "these are the people that came to see us in that airplane." Mrs. Alsop raised her finger, and the strangers bent their antennae down in her direction.

"This is Mr. Rafferty," Mrs. Alsop said. "He's a newspaper reporter. He wanted to see your airplane."

Rafferty nodded. The strangers curled up their antennae and nodded politely. The woman scratched her side with her claws.

Rafferty tried to keep his voice steady. "What—uh—did you say their names are, Mrs. Alsop?" he asked.

"Well, we don't know," Mrs. Alsop said. "You see, they can only make pictures for you. They point those funny horns at you, and they just think. That makes you think, too—the same thing they're thinking. I asked them what their name is. Then I let them think to me. All I saw was a picture of a man with a hammer, molding some iron. So their name is perhaps something like Man-Who-Bends-Iron."

"Do you suppose," Rafferty said, "they would talk to me—or *think* to me?"

Mrs. Alsop looked puzzled. "I suppose they'd be glad to, Mr. Rafferty. The only thing is, it's pretty hard at first to see what they're thinking in their brain."

"I'll try," said Rafferty. "Ask these— uh—people where they come from."

Mrs. Alsop raised her finger politely to the woman. The flexible antenna on the lady's head bent toward Mrs. Alsop and aimed at her head.

"This young man," Mrs. Alsop said in a loud voice, "wants to know where you people come from."

Mr. Alsop nudged Rafferty. "Just hold up your finger when you want your answer."

Rafferty felt awfully silly, but he held up his finger. The woman bent her antenna down until they aimed on Rafferty between the eyes. Suddenly his brain felt as though it were made of flexible rubber. It seemed as if someone were wringing it all out of shape and molding it back together again. He thought he was flying through space as stars and comets whirled by, and a great, white, blinking star stood there in his mind. Then it went out.

"Mr. Rafferty, did you get your answer?" Mr. Alsop asked.

"Mr. Alsop!" Rafferty cried. "Mrs. Alsop! This is on the level! These creatures are really from outer space!"

Mr. Alsop said, "Sure, they have come a long way."

"Do you know this is the most amazing thing that has ever happened? It points to the biggest story in the world!" Rafferty yelled. "Where is your phone?"

"We don't have a telephone," Mr. Alsop said. "There's one down the road a piece. But these people are going to leave in a few minutes. Why don't you wait and see them off?"

"No!" Rafferty gulped. "They can't go in a few minutes! Listen, I've got to phone— get someone to come with a camera!"

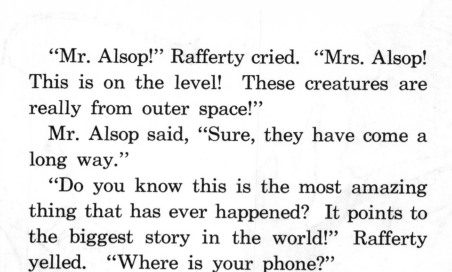

"Well," said Mrs. Alsop, "we tried to get them to stay over for supper. But they have to go at a certain time. They have to catch a tide or something like that."

"It's the moon," Mr. Alsop said. "It's something about the moon being in the right place."

The creatures from outer space sat with their claws folded in their laps. Their antennae were politely folded to show they weren't trying to see what other people were thinking.

Rafferty looked carefully over the room.

"Listen, Alsop," he whispered, "you got a camera? Any kind of a camera?" Then he shouted, "I've got to have a camera!"

"Oh, sure," Mr. Alsop said. "I got a fine camera. It's a box camera, but it takes good pictures. I'll show you some I took of my chickens."

"No, no! I don't want to see your good pictures. I want the camera!"

Mr. Alsop went into the bedroom.

"Mrs. Alsop!" Rafferty shouted. "I've got to get lots of information!"

"Okay," Mrs. Alsop said merrily. "These folks won't mind."

"Ethel, you seen my camera?" Mr. Alsop called from the bedroom.

Mrs. Alsop sighed. "No, I haven't. You're the one that put it away last."

"Only trouble is," Mr. Alsop said, "I haven't got any film for it."

Suddenly the creatures from outer space turned their antennae toward each other for a second. Then they got up and darted here and there about the room as quick as bees. They were scurrying so fast Rafferty could hardly see them. Then they darted out the door and off toward the barn.

Rafferty rushed out the door and hollered at the creatures to stop. But the shiny plastic contraption slid out of the barn. S-s-s-s-ch! The thing lifted mysteriously out of sight into the clouds.

Rafferty just stood there in the mud. The creatures were gone. All that was left was a steaming place in the mud and a little circle of burned earth. He had no pictures, no way to prove what he had seen, and no story. Suddenly he had the craziest idea. He went scurrying toward the house.

"Alsop!" he yelled. "Did those people pay for the eggs?"

"Oh, sure," he answered. "Perhaps, in a way, they did."

"Let me see the money!" Rafferty said.

"Oh, not in money," Mr. Alsop said. "They don't have any money. But when they were here six years ago, they brought us some eggs to trade for ours."

"Six years ago!" Rafferty moaned. Then he started. "Eggs! What kind of eggs?"

Mr. Alsop folded his arms and grinned. "Oh, craziest things you ever saw," he said. "We called them star ducks. The eggs were shaped like stars. We set them under a hen, and she hatched 'em. But those star points poked at the old hen something awful."

"A star duck isn't much good, though," Mr. Alsop continued. "It looks something like a baby hippopotamus and a little bit like a swallow. It has six legs. Only two of the star ducks lived, though, and we ate them for Thanksgiving."

Rafferty was still worrying about a way for him to prove to the world that he had seen people from outer space.

"Mr. Alsop," he whispered, "I suppose you wouldn't know where the skeletons of the star ducks are?"

Mr. Alsop looked puzzled. "Skeletons? You mean the bones? We gave the bones to the dog. That was five years ago. Even the dog is dead now. I know where the dog's bones are though."

Rafferty picked up his hat, his face a pale blank. "Thanks, Mr. Alsop," he said in a whisper. "Thanks a lot."

Rafferty stood on the porch and put on his hat.

Mr. Alsop opened the door and came out, blowing the dust off a box camera.

"Oh, Mr. Rafferty," he said. "I found my camera."

Think about This:

1 In English, what is the last name that came from "Man-Who-Bends-Iron"?
2 How did Rafferty know that the creatures were from outer space?
3 What else could the duck skeletons have been used for besides proof that Rafferty had really seen space creatures?
4 What are some things that have happened that have made some men believe that space creatures have really visited the earth?

remake　repaid　returns

tightness　kindness　stiffness

witnesses　dries　watches

delight　delay　depart

payment　argument　contentment

glider　chasing　using　ruled

false　blouse　verse

Christopher　luncheon

remove

shortness

branches

delighted

excitement

exercising

case

spinney

Woozle

continue

Pooh and Piglet
Go Hunting

One fine winter's day when Piglet was brushing away the snow in front of his house, he happened to look up, and there was Winnie-the-Pooh. Pooh was walking round and round in a circle, thinking of something else, and when Piglet called to him, he just went on walking.

"Hallo!" said Piglet, "what are *you* doing?"

"Hunting," said Pooh.

"Hunting what?"

"Tracking something," said Winnie-the-Pooh very mysteriously.

"Tracking what?" said Piglet, coming closer.

"That's just what I ask myself. I ask myself, What?"

"What do you think you'll answer?"

"I shall have to wait until I catch up with it," said Winnie-the-Pooh. "Now, look there." He pointed to the ground in front of him. "What do you see there?"

"Tracks," said Piglet. "Paw-marks." He gave a little squeak of excitement. "Oh, Pooh! Do you think it's a–a–a Woozle?"

"It may be," said Pooh. "Sometimes it is, and sometimes it isn't. You never can tell with paw-marks."

With these few words he went on tracking, and Piglet, after watching him for a minute or two, ran after him. Winnie-the-Pooh had come to a sudden stop, and was bending over the tracks in a puzzled sort of way.

"What's the matter?" asked Piglet.

"It's a very funny thing," said Bear, "but there seem to be *two* animals now. This—whatever-it-was—has been joined by another—whatever-it-is—and the two of them are now proceeding in company. Would you mind coming with me, Piglet, in case they turn out to be Hostile Animals?"

Piglet scratched his ear in a nice sort of way, and said that he had nothing to do until Friday, and would be delighted to come, in case it really *was* a Woozle.

"You mean, in case it really is two Woozles," said Winnie-the-Pooh, and Piglet said that anyhow he had nothing to do until Friday. So off they went together.

There was a small spinney of larch trees just here, and it seemed as if the two Woozles, if that is what they were, had been going round this spinney; so round this spinney went Pooh and Piglet after them; Piglet passing the time by telling Pooh what his Grandfather Trespassers W had done to Remove Stiffness after Tracking, and how his Grandfather Trespassers W had suffered in his later years from Shortness of Breath, and other matters of interest, and Pooh wondering what a Grandfather was like, and if perhaps this was Two Grandfathers they were after now, and, if so, whether he would be allowed to take one home and keep it, and what Christopher Robin would say. And still the tracks went on in front of them. . . .

Suddenly Winnie-the-Pooh stopped, and pointed excitedly in front of him. *"Look!"*

"What?" said Piglet, with a jump. And then, to show that he hadn't been frightened, he jumped up and down once or twice in an exercising sort of way.

"The tracks!" said Pooh. "*A third animal has joined the other two!*"

"Pooh!" cried Piglet. "Do you think it is another Woozle?"

"No," said Pooh, "because it makes different marks. It is either Two Woozles and one, as it might be, Wizzle, or Two, as it might be, Wizzles and one, if so it is, Woozle. Let us continue to follow them."

So they went on, feeling just a little anxious now, in case the three animals in front of them were of Hostile Intent. And Piglet wished very much that his Grandfather T. W. were there, instead of elsewhere, and Pooh thought how nice it would be if they met Christopher Robin suddenly but quite accidentally, and only because he liked Christopher Robin so much. And then, all of a sudden, Winnie-the-Pooh stopped again, and licked the tip of his nose in a cooling manner, for he was feeling more hot and anxious than ever in his life before. *There were four animals in front of them!*

"Do you see, Piglet? Look at their tracks! Three, as it were, Woozles, and one, as it was, Wizzle. *Another Woozle has joined them!*"

And so it seemed to be. There were the tracks; crossing over each other here, getting muddled up with each other there; but, quite plainly every now and then, the tracks of four sets of paws.

"I *think*," said Piglet, when he had licked the tip of his nose too, and found that it brought very little comfort, "I *think* that I have just remembered something. I have just remembered something that I forgot to do yesterday and shan't be able to do tomorrow. So I suppose I really ought to go back and do it now."

"We'll do it this afternoon, and I'll come with you," said Pooh.

"It isn't the sort of thing you can do in the afternoon," said Piglet quickly. "It's a very particular morning thing, that has to be done in the morning, and, if possible, between the hours of— What would you say the time was?"

"About twelve," said Winnie-the-Pooh, looking at the sun.

"Between, as I was saying, the hours of twelve and twelve five. So, really, dear old Pooh, if you'll excuse me— *What's that?*"

Pooh looked up at the sky, and then, as he heard the whistle again, he looked up into the branches of a big oak-tree, and then he saw a friend of his.

"It's Christopher Robin," he said.

"Ah, then you'll be all right," said
Piglet. "You'll be quite safe with *him*.
Good-bye," and he trotted off home as
quickly as he could, very glad to be Out
of All Danger again.

Christopher Robin came slowly down his tree. "Silly old Bear," he said, "what *were* you doing? First you went round the spinney twice by yourself, and then Piglet ran after you and you went round again together, and then you were just going round a fourth time—"

"Wait a moment," said Winnie-the-Pooh, holding up his paw.

He sat down and thought, in the most thoughtful way he could think. Then he fitted his paw into one of the Tracks . . . and then he scratched his nose twice, and stood up.

"Yes," said Winnie-the-Pooh.

"I see now," said Winnie-the-Pooh.

"I have been Foolish and Deluded," said he, "and I am a Bear of No Brain at All."

"You're the Best Bear in All the World," said Christopher Robin soothingly.

"Am I?" said Pooh hopefully. And then he brightened up suddenly.

"Anyhow," he said, "it is nearly Luncheon Time."

So he went home for it.

The Trial
of Mother Goose

by Helen Louise Miller

CAST

Old King Cole
Queen
Cook
Mary, *the maid*
Peter, the *pipe-maker*
Felix, *fiddler*
Freddy, *fiddler*
Fritz, *fiddler*
Mother Goose

Mistress Mary
Little Boy Blue
Miss Muffet
Old Woman in
  the Shoe
Two Soldiers
Herald
Three Children

SETTING

The kitchen of King Cole's palace

Scene I

Mary: There! This bowl is as bright as I can make it.

Cook: Why are you working so hard, Mary? King Cole hasn't called for his bowl in weeks.

Mary: I want to have it ready for him, just in case.

Peter: That's why I'm making him a new pipe.   He must be tired of his old ones. He never sends for them any more.

Cook: There's something wrong around here!   I smell trouble!

Felix: Hmmm!   Something smells good!

Cook: Out of my way, Felix.   This is no place for three lazy fiddlers!

Fritz: But we're not lazy.   It's not our fault the King hasn't called for us.

Freddy: We came to help.   Isn't there something we can do?

Peter: Why don't you go practice your music or write a new tune?

Freddy: What's the use?   King Cole wouldn't even let us play it!

Cook: The King is not himself these days.
He is never pleased any more.

All: Old King Cole is a grumpy old soul,
And a grumpy old soul is he.
He won't have his pipe,
And he won't have his bowl,
And he won't have his fiddlers three!

Queen: And he won't even talk to me!

Felix: Pardon us, Your Majesty.

Freddy: We didn't mean to be making fun
of the King.

Fritz: But he really is grumpy!

Cook: There's no way to please him.

Mary: We're worried about him.

Queen: So am I! Cole was always such a
merry soul! And now he doesn't ever laugh
or smile!

Peter: The King has everything to make
him happy.

Mary: Not an enemy in the world! He has
endeared himself to all.

Queen: But that's the trouble. He says he
does have an enemy! An enemy who must
be hunted down and brought to him in
chains before he will smile again.

Peter: Who is it?

Queen: I have no idea.

Mary: Every man, woman, and child in the kingdom loves Old King Cole.

Mother Goose: Help!   Let me in!

Cook: Quick!   Peter, open the door!

Mother Goose: Oh, please, hide me!   Hide me!   They're after me!

Queen: Hush, good woman. Do not be afraid. You're among friends. Now, sit down. Tell us who you are and who's chasing you.

Mother Goose: The soldiers are chasing me! The King's men!

Felix: What have you done?

Mother Goose: I have done nothing to harm a soul. I am only a poor old woman.

Queen: What is your name?

Mother Goose: My name is Mother Goose. All my life I have written verses for little children. Oh, please, won't you hide me from the soldiers?

First Soldier: Open! In the King's name!

Mother Goose: Soldiers! Please hide me!

Queen: Quick! Under the table!

First Soldier: Where is she?

Second Soldier: We saw her come in here!

First Soldier: Hand her over!

Second Soldier: By order of the King!

Queen: Now what is the meaning of this?

First Soldier: Pardon, Your Majesty. We are on the trail of the King's enemy.

Second Soldier: He ordered us to bring her in—dead or alive!

Queen: You must be mistaken. Such a poor old woman.

First Soldier: Then Your Majesty has seen her!

Second Soldier: She did come in here!

King Cole: What is the meaning of this? What goes on here?

First Soldier: We've tracked the old woman through the palace grounds, Sire.

Second Soldier: She must have hidden in this very room.

King Cole: Then find her. What are you waiting for?

Queen: Sire, I will not stand by and see a poor old woman hunted down. You certainly must be mistaken.

Herald: Look, Your Majesty! Look at the table! It's moving!

King Cole: Aha! So, there you are!

Queen: Please, Sire, let her go!

Mother Goose: It's no use! It's no use!

King Cole: Watch the prisoner, men.

scrubbed fanned permitted   whipped

costly partly swiftly   bravely

rainy misty airy   guilty

crushes mixes touches   witnesses

contrary

curds

sword dungeon statue   innocent

justice

victory

insulting

Scene II

King Cole: Herald, read the charges made against this woman!

Herald: The prisoner has been charged with writing silly and insulting verses about King Cole and other important people.

King Cole: You have heard the charges, Mother Goose. How do you plead? Innocent or guilty?

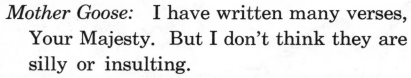

Mother Goose: I have written many verses, Your Majesty. But I don't think they are silly or insulting.

King Cole: Make a note, Herald. She says she wrote the verses. We will now take up that verse she wrote about me!

Queen: Everyone knows that, Sire. "Old King Cole was a merry old soul, and a merry old soul was he—

Peter: "He called for his pipe—

Mary: "He called for his bowl—

Fiddlers: "And he called for his fiddlers three!"

Queen: Now, what is so silly or insulting about that?

King Cole: It makes me look foolish, as if I spend all my time at food, drink, and music! I want the world to know about my great works—the people I have saved, the laws I've made, the battles I've won! And besides all that, I'm not old! I'm only thirty-nine!

Mother Goose: But, Your Majesty—

King Cole: Quiet! Herald, it's time for the witnesses. You may show them in!

Herald: Mistress Mary! Little Boy Blue! Little Miss Muffet! The Old Woman in the Shoe!

King: Mistress Mary, what is your claim against Mother Goose?

Mistress Mary: It's her fault that people call me "Contrary Mary." All because of that silly verse —"Mistress Mary, quite contrary, how does your garden grow?"

King Cole: Little Boy Blue, what is your claim?

Little Boy Blue: It's her fault I can't get a job! No one wants me to mind their sheep because she said I was under the haystack fast asleep!

King Cole: Little Miss Muffet will state her case.

Miss Muffet: It's her fault folks think I'm a fraidy-cat because she said I ran away from a spider!

King Cole: The last of our witnesses is the Old Woman Who Lived in a Shoe.

Old Woman: It's her fault that everyone thinks I'm mean to my children. She wrote that I gave them some soup without any bread, whipped all the children, and sent them to bed!

King Cole: You have heard the charges of the people, Mother Goose. What do you say for yourself?

Mother Goose: Not a thing, Your Majesty. I only wrote the truth.

King Cole: In that case, the case is now closed. You stand guilty as charged.

Queen: No, Your Majesty! She's innocent!

King Cole: She has been found guilty, but I will give her one more chance!

Queen: Thank you, Sire.

King Cole: I asked each of our witnesses to bring his own verse of cockleshells, silver bells, curds and whey, and other such things. If Mother Goose will sign these new verses and will agree to have them put in all the Mother Goose books from now on, we will set her free. Do you agree?

Mother Goose: I must hear the new verses before I can say.

King Cole: Very well. We will start with Mistress Mary.

Mistress Mary:
Mistress Mary, light and airy,
How does your garden grow?
With cockleshells and silver bells,
And pretty maids all in a row.

Little Boy Blue:

Little Boy Blue is blowing his horn
To keep the animals out of the corn.
He is the one to look after your sheep,
Always alert, and never asleep!

Miss Muffet:

Little Miss Muffet, she sat on a tuffet,
Eating of curds and whey.
There came a great spider, who sat down
    beside her,
But bravely, Miss Muffet did stay!

Old Woman:

There was a woman who lived in a shoe.
For children she knew just what to do.
She fed them their supper and put them
    to bed,
Giving each dear a pat on the head!

King Cole: For myself, I have written this verse!

Great King Cole was a very fine soul,
And a very fine soul was he!
He called for his sword,
And he called for his gun,
And he marched off to victory!

Herald: Now, just sign this paper right here, my good woman.

Mother Goose: Never! Never! Never! I will be your prisoner forever rather than sign a paper full of lies!

King Cole: Then go to the dungeon! You've had your chance! Off to the dungeon!

Scene III

Children: No! No! No! No!

King Cole: What is that shouting? Where is it coming from?

Queen: Out there, Your Majesty.

King Cole: Where? I can't see anyone.

Queen: Way out there, Sire. Now they are coming closer.

King Cole: Who are you out there?

First Child: We are the children of the world!

Second Child: We demand to be heard!

King Cole: Come here where I can see you. What do you want?

Third Child: We want justice!

First Child: Mother Goose has endeared herself to all the children of the world. We are here to plead for her.

Mistress Mary: But our new verses are so much better than the old ones.

First Child: That's because you're too contrary to know any better!

Mistress Mary: I am not contrary!

Children: Yes, you are!

Second Child: That's why we love you!

Third Child: That's why you're famous!

Mistress Mary: Me? Famous?

First Child: Of course. Mother Goose has made every one of you famous all over the world.

Little Boy Blue: Don't people mind that I fell asleep?

Second Child: They wouldn't like you half so much if you had stayed awake!

Miss Muffet: And what about me? Do they make fun of me because I ran away from a spider?

Third Child: Lots of girls are afraid of a spider.

Old Woman: How about me? Do children know I really love them?

Children: Yes, indeed!

Old Woman: If this is what the children of the world think of us, Your Majesty, we must set Mother Goose free.

Witnesses: Agreed.

King Cole: But what about me? It is all very well for you to take back all your charges against Mother Goose. But I am the King, and I demand to be treated with respect!

Queen: But, Sire, they love you best of all.

First Child: We read about lots of kings who have won battles. But half the time, we can't even remember their names.

First Soldier: Everywhere I travel I see your statue on park grounds and in public places.

Second Soldier: There are always plenty of hostile kings around, but it's hard to find a jolly one, like you!

King Cole: I'm beginning to feel a bit merry again.

Children: Three cheers for King Cole!

King Cole: Mother Goose, I give to you a full pardon! Herald, I wish to make this news public.

Hear ye! Hear ye! From this day,
Mother Goose shall hold full sway.
Honor her when she appears,
Meet her with delighted cheers!
Don't forget the one who named us,
Mother Goose, who made us famous!

Mother Goose: Thank you, King Cole!

King Cole: Peter, my pipe! Mary, my bowl! Mother Goose, here's to you. And now, for my fiddlers three! I order you to play a merry tune!

ACKNOWLEDGMENTS

Grateful acknowledgment is given for permission to adapt and reprint the following copyrighted material:

"All Champs Wear Lucky Sneakers" by Lydia Grabowski. Adapted by special permission from *Jack and Jill* Magazine © 1967 The Curtis Publishing Company.

"Amazing Underground City" adapted from "America's Amazing Underground City" by Edward Hymoff, *Boys' Life*, August 1963. Reprinted by permission of the author and *Boys' Life*, published by the Boy Scouts of America.

"Any Old Junk Today?" adapted from *Little Eddie* by Carolyn Haywood. Adapted by permission of William Morrow & Company, Inc. Copyright 1947 by William Morrow and Company, Inc.

"Billy and the Power Mower" by Marion Holland. Original version published in *Story Parade*, September 1953; this adaptation by permission of the author.

"Blue Faces and Star Bones" adapted from "The Star Ducks" by Bill Brown. Copyright 1950 by Fantasy House, Inc. Reprinted from *The Magazine of Fantasy and Science Fiction*.

"By Flume to Chico" adapted from "The Magnificent Descent" by Richard M. Murdock; *Boys' Life*, August 1962. By permission of the author and *Boys' Life*, published by the Boy Scouts of America.

"Cloud Horses" reprinted from *God's Wonderful World* by John Travers Moore, 1964, by permission of Augsburg Publishing House, Minneapolis, Minnesota, copyright owners.

"Danny and the Rangers" adapted from the story "A Home for Danny" by Ruth Gipson Plowhead from *Story Parade Magazine*, copyright 1940, copyright renewed 1968 by Story Parade, Inc. By permission of Western Publishing Company, Inc.

"A Dream That Ran on Steam" adapted from "The Hustling Dream That Ran on Steam" by Lyman M. Nash, *Boys'* Life, December 1963. By permission of the author and *Boys' Life*, published by the Boy Scouts or America.

"The Emperor's New Clothes" adapted from *Andersen's Fairy Tales* translated by Valdemar Paulsen. Copyright 1916, renewal copyright 1944, Rand McNally & Company.

"For Mary Ellis" adapted from "Mary Ellis Has a Birthday Party" from *Steppin and Family* by Hope Newell. Used by permission of James M. Newell.

"Funny the Way Different Cars Start" reprinted from *I Like Machinery* by Dorothy W. Baruch, published by Harper & Brothers. Used by permission of Bertha Klausner International Literary Agency, Inc.

"Ghost Horses" adapted from "Ghost Horses on Giant's Backbone" by Ann Boyle. *Wee Wisdom*, May 1963. Used by permission of the publisher.

"Henry Uses His Head" adapted from "Henry's Canine Teeth" from *Henry and Ribsy* by Beverly Cleary. Adapted by permission of William Morrow and Company, Inc. Copyright © 1954 by Beverly Cleary.

"In My New Clothing" reprinted from *The Four Seasons* by Basho. Used by permission of Peter Pauper Press, Inc.

"An Introduction to Dogs" reprinted from *I'm a Stranger Here Myself* by Ogden Nash. Copyright, 1938, by Ogden Nash. By permission of Little, Brown and Company and Ogden Nash.

"Kate and the Big Cat" adapted from "Tiger in the Lake" by Edward Kurkul. Adapted by permission from *Jack and Jill* Magazine. © 1964 The Curtis Publishing Company.

"Leaf Painter" from "The Leaf Painter" by David Hoxworth, adapted by permission from *Jack and Jill* Magazine, © 1974 by The Saturday Evening Post Company.

"Lisa's Song" by Ruth Kennell, *Story Parade*, July 1941. Copyright 1941 by Story Parade, Inc. Reprinted and adapted by permission of Western Publishing Company, Inc.

"Mr. Mudgett's Invention" by Judith Gold. Adapted by special permission from *Jack and Jill* Magazine © 1965 The Curtis Publishing Company.

"Pooh and Piglet Go Hunting" from the book *Winnie-the-Pooh* by A. A. Milne, copyright 1926 by E. P. Dutton & Co., Inc., renewal 1954 by A. A. Milne. Mr. C. R. Milne, copyright holder. Reprinted by permission of E. P. Dutton & Co., Inc. and Methuen Children's Books Ltd., publishers.

"Rooftop Secret" adapted from "A Green Plant" by Frances Poth. Adapted by special permission from *Jack and Jill* Magazine © 1967 The Curtis Publishing Company.

ILLUSTRATORS

Bill Carr, Ted Carr, Gus Colichidas, Linda Strauss Edwards, Jon Goodell, Lowell Herrero, Tom Hill, David Kerr, Rebecca Lusk, William Mathison, Tom Newsom, Louise Price, Philip Smith, Al Stine, Joe Szeghy, Jerry Warshoski, Floyd Webb, Charles Wishowski.